# Praise for Forest Bathing with Y...

"Lovely in many ways: The book, The subject, The practice, The author."

— Willem Lange, host of PBS' award-winning "Windows to the Wild" television show

"After reading this book, I understand the genius behind Nadine's innovative combination of forest bathing and dog walking, a combined practice that elevates the meaning and joy of each! As a person with a lifelong appreciation for the power of immersing oneself in nature and one who has been lucky enough to experience guided walks led by Nadine, I'm so glad you've picked up this book! In exploring the world through the eyes of the wise and playful duo of Nadine and Juliet, your life is also apt to take a rejuvenating turn."

— Melanie Choukas-Bradley, Author of The Joy of Forest Bathing—Reconnect with Wild Places & Rejuvenate Your Life

"Nadine, your journey has provided me with new eyes when out with our dog, Brooke. Brooke is truly a project dog—she is intelligent and impulsive—both of which can get her in a pickle in human society. Forest bathing for Brooke helps her cope and keeps her sanity in check."

— Sue Schiemer, Certified Forest Therapy Guide, Educator, and Student of Positive Reinforcement Training

"I'm so grateful for what you've shared about forest bathing with a dog. Luna and I had a GREAT time! I felt very attuned to her, and I believe she felt the same toward me. One of the best moments was when Luna was exploring an old stone wall. She spent considerable time sticking her nose into all the spaces between the rocks—and snorting and smelling in a highly attentive way. It actually made me think of the way human detectives seek clues regarding who has been in a place and what has happened there. I loved participating as a silent sharer in Luna's quest to explore the inner spaces of the stone wall. This made me so grateful for you!"

— Candace Anderson, Artist

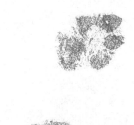

# Forest Bathing with your Dog

### By
### Nadine Mazzola

*Foreword by*
*Melanie Choukas-Bradley*

Forest Bathing with your Dog
by Nadine Mazzola

Library of Congress Control Number:2019908770
Print ISBN: 978-1-7332110-3-1
Ebook ISBN: 978-1-7332110-1-7

Publisher: Blue Cloud Books
Phone 1-978-549-2505
nenft.com/blue-cloud-books

Cover design by Nadine Mazzola
Book design by Nadine Mazzola
Photo credits: Nadine Mazzola,
Jerry Mazzola, Jerry Borofsky
Book trailer videography: Annabel O'Neill

# Contents

### Juliet

Can I just tell you,
how much I love walking in the woods with you.
The wanders, the pauses, the adventures, the sit spots,
you speak the language of the forest beings.
There is always something new that you show me.
My heart smiles and I feel like singing
as we wander and explore.
Can I just tell you,
thank you, little one.

To my husband, Jerry,
who has held my hand with loving grace
and offered inspiration and encouragement
through all our adventures both good and bad.

And to the FOREST
Thank you both for having my back.

# Foreword

by Melanie Choukas-Bradley

Nadine Mazzola guided one of my very first forest bathing walks, beginning in a lilac grove in full bloom. She invited our forest bathing group to freely wander the fragrant grove, sticking our noses into every colorful cluster of lilacs we could find. We then wandered down an open hillside and into a wooded stream valley where Nadine gave us time to soak up the beauty of the water flowing under the trees. She invited us to create ephemeral works of art from sticks, stones, wildflowers, and other natural materials. While we made art destined to be washed away by the rain, Nadine foraged for leaves and flowers for the tea she then served us under the trees.

Nadine made us feel as though we had all the time in the world to enjoy the beauty and wonder surrounding us. And that's just what she does in the pages of this book. Told both through her own voice and the voice of her beloved dog, Juliet, this inspiring, poignant, and playful book invites you to pause (or "paws"!) in your busy daily life to enjoy the natural beauty and intrigue that await just outside your door.

In exploring the world through the eyes of the wise and playful duo of Nadine and Juliet, your life is also apt to take a rejuvenating turn.

As we learn through the affectionate canine voice of Juliet, Nadine Mazzola had a richly faceted life before she became the first Certified Forest Therapy Guide in New England in 2015. Not only did she have a successful career in business and marketing, she is a former world professional pocket billiards player who competed on the Women's Professional Billiard Tour.

That walk Nadine led in the lilac grove and stream valley of the arboretum in the Berkshire Mountains was part of my own training to become a Certified Forest Therapy Guide. When I learned that Nadine was leading forest bathing walks *with Juliet* for other people and their dogs I was intrigued! And after reading this book, I understand the genius behind Nadine's innovative combination of forest bathing and dog-walking, a combined practice that elevates the meaning and joy of each!

Dogs naturally do what we humans strive to do on the forest bathing walks that began in Japan in the 1980s and have since become popular around the world. When we humans are in the forest, we have to let go of daily distractions to become fully present in the moment. Dogs are already there. We have to remind ourselves to stop and smell the roses, while a dog wouldn't dream of passing up a tempting scent. Dogs are mindfully present for all they encounter in the forest, and they have much to teach us.

Nadine learns the art of being fully, curiously, and appreciatively present from Juliet. It seems that about the only thing Nadine has to teach Juliet is the art of *relaxed forest-sitting*. As Juliet opines from her canine perspective: "All dogs can learn new tricks, but sometimes it takes time…It took me a while to get the hang of [relaxed forest-sitting]. At first, I was very restless. 'Why should we just sit when we could be investigating or chasing things?' There are days when [Nadine] is restless, too. But I've noticed that as one of us relaxes, the other follows suit, and we both sink in to a blissful, watchful state. Sometimes I wind my leash around a tree or other object so that if one of us shifts position we're not disturbing the other."

While you romp with Nadine and Juliet through these pages, you'll experience some serious currents interwoven with the playfulness. As Juliet lets you know up front, Nadine is a breast cancer survivor. The health benefits of forest bathing that have been documented in studies around the world attracted her to the practice. As Juliet recalls, "One day [Nadine] heard someone mention forest bathing and how being under the forest canopy boosted the Natural Killer (NK) cells in human immune systems. I didn't know it in that moment, but our lives would take on a new turn after that day."

Juliet describes the early days of Nadine's treatment, which involved three surgeries, chemotherapy, and radiation: "I'd put my cutest face on and wiggle *just* enough to get a bit of a smile from her. This often led to a trip outside for us both. The fresh air always brought energy and smiles. Most days we would go across the street, into the woods. We wouldn't go far, but just being among the trees made us both feel alive and connected to other living things."

As a person with a lifelong appreciation for the power of immersing oneself in nature and one who has been lucky enough to experience guided walks led by my mentor and fellow forest therapy guide, Nadine, I'm so glad you've picked up this book. In exploring the world through the eyes of the wise and playful duo of Nadine and Juliet, your life is also apt to take a rejuvenating turn.

— *Melanie Choukas-Bradley*

Melanie is an award-winning author and well-known naturalist and forest therapy guide in the Washington, DC, area. She has written five wonderful books the most recent of which was The Joy of Forest Bathing: Reconnect With Wild Places & Rejuvenate Your Life. If you live or are visiting the Washington DC area, check out her website for one of her upcoming events: melaniechoukas-bradley.com.

# Welcome!

As odd as this may sound, I wrote this book with my dog, Juliet. She is both my beloved dog and one of my mentors. Juliet, as it happens, is a natural forest bathing guru. All dogs are natural forest bathing gurus. In our years together, Juliet has been inviting and inspiring me, leading me deeper and deeper into the practice of forest bathing. It's not difficult. Turns out I just needed to pay attention.

Juliet and I share the storytelling in our book and so we needed a way to distinguish our voices for you, the reader. Juliet's sections begin with *"In Juliet's words"* and because Juliet also loves the mud, we decided that when Juliet is speaking, there would be a background of grey in honor of her love for mud. While this book is a guide for forest bathing with your dog, it is not a book on how to train your dog. Rather it is a book on how to be with your dog while practicing forest bathing. It is also a bit of a love story about our relationships with our dogs, the forests we walk in, and the land.

In this book, Juliet and I share our personal story and how we came to forest bathing in **Our Authors' Journey**. This section is told by Juliet in her own words since she's such a good storyteller. **Section 1** focuses on what forest bathing is and what forest bathing looks and feels like. Juliet and I share some first-hand forest bathing experiences. **Section 2** is where we share how to forest bathe with your dog, what that is like, and some useful tips. **Section 3** discusses how forest bathing benefits your dog (and you, too). **Section 4** gives you a forest bathing field guide and some wonderful reflections from other dog owners on forest bathig with their dogs. There is even a **Bonus Section** on Forest Bathing with Cats. *Enjoy!*

# Our Authors' Journeys

*In Juliet's Words*

**First—My Story**

My name is Juliet, and although I had a bit of a "ruff" start in life, I must say that at key moments, luck and love have come my way. (Please excuse the pun, but being a dog, I just love puns.) My human mom and dad adopted me from the North-East Animal Shelter in Salem, Massachusetts. A no-kill shelter and a lovely place, I was nonetheless very happy to be leaving for my forever home. My siblings and I originally hailed from Puerto Rico. When we were six weeks old, we were all taken in by a human foster parent who cared for us until we were four months old and able to travel north to Massachusetts to be adopted. This involved an incredibly scary airplane ride, which I don't recommend to anyone. If you're curious, my ancestry is a bit of Britney Spaniel, Curly Coated Retriever, and a wee bit of Pekingese. I'm eight in dog years (fifty-six in human years) and weigh 28-pounds. I tend to be a dog of few words, but my human mom, Nadine, helped me find my writing voice as we created this book together.

I remember the moment when my human mom and dad and I first met. It was love at first sight. I was a bouncy, young pup and mom bent down to greet me. We locked eyes as if we already knew each other from a long time ago. A deep soul connection. Do you know the kind I mean? Her warm, sweet, blue eyes met my big, brown pools of love. Our instant bond recognized, we both simultaneously looked up at my human-dad-to-be, and then he knew it, too. We all decided to adopt each other in that moment, and we've been a great trio ever since.

We've traveled lots of miles since that day. Many of them during our daily walks in the woods on the nearby trails of our town, Acton, Massachusetts. Mom is so joyous to be in the woods. Being under the forest canopy daily has a huge positive effect on us both. Mom says it is an unexpected benefit of having a dog in her life again. The sun shining through the treetops and the many shades of green. The sounds of birds and leaves rustling in the wind. And the smells. All those amazing smells.

**Mom's Story**

Mom grew up with a love and curiosity for many things, among them gardening and the forest. This was partly her own nature as a child but also something that was passed along to her from her family. She and her mom would walk in the woods and instead of identify things, her mother would point out things that she was drawn to and share her enjoyment of the beauty she experienced. Her dad was the first one to teach her the practice of gratitude for nature's gifts and giving thanks. Her stepmom brought her sense of play to the forest and they would make placemats out of ferns or dress up like fairies and dance in the forest. Her aunt and uncle had a big garden, and every Christmas, Nadine received a packet of mixed seeds in her Christmas stocking that she could look forward to planting in her very own plot of that garden. She would visit her garden throughout the growing season to help tend her plot and see how things were growing and changing. Her grandparents shared a broader sense of wonder and the pleasure of simply taking time to sit and observe.

But as kids grow into young adults they can often temporarily forget these moments, and this was the case with Mom. It had been some years since Mom had been in the forest regularly, and this was one of my gifts to her. She didn't realize it yet, but this is when **I began** her forest bathing training. When I was a young pup we explored the woods near our house together and mapped the trails with our minds and noses. We found wide open spaces and secret little nooks in which to sit and watch things.

When mom and dad adopted me, it was a tough time in their lives. My adopted grandmother was suffering with dementia. A disease that is so hard on everyone involved and unfortunately, more and more common today. Mom would tell me that I was such a gift because I brought tons of love to the family during that very difficult time. One of mom's ways of coping was to be in the woods and we

> "One of the most fundamental lessons of cancer is to recognize the distinction between being cured and being healed.

went there frequently to find comfort. I suppose it won't surprise you that my mom, Nadine, and her mom walked in the woods a lot as well, both when mom was a wee pup and as something they enjoyed together as adults. Mom also realized that even when her mom's dementia became advanced and she could no longer speak, being outdoors was one of the things she still enjoyed the most.

9

However, that was not to be our only challenge. In our third year together, mom was diagnosed with breast cancer. As you can imagine the road through treatment was hard and long and included a year of chemotherapy, radiation and three surgeries. Those were tough months. Mom felt sick a lot and it was hard for her to eat or drink much of anything. I remember Dad would go to the store and buy twelve different kinds of drinks in hopes that one of them would taste good to mom. Dad is just that kind of guy.

Dad and I stuck really close to mom during this time and I rarely left her side. I tried to do my share and help mom keep her strength and spirits up by inspiring her to get outside. I'd put my cutest face on and wiggle just enough to get a bit of a smile from her. This often led to a trip outside for us both. The fresh air always brought energy and smiles. Most days we would go across the street into the woods. We wouldn't go far but just being among the trees made us both feel alive and connected to other living things. We'd wander, sit, and wander some more. It was winter and there was a lot of snow that year. Mom would bundle up in ski pants, her warmest jacket, two hats, two neck warmers and her warmest mittens. She looked very cute.

Treatment for her breast cancer was successful and we were on our way to recovery, but mom and I would discover that healing from the cancer experience, the trauma of its treatment regimen, and living with the uncertainty of the future was another thing altogether. Transitioning from in-treatment to post-treatment felt both happy and frightening all at once. It became its own new journey, a journey of another sort of healing. One of mom's mentors, Candace Anderson, also a cancer survivor, wrote this about healing and cancer.

"One of the most fundamental lessons of cancer is to recognize the distinction between being cured and being healed. It is quite natural to want to be cured of an illness; however, the irony about focusing on being cured is this–the only way you know if you're cured, is if your cancer comes back–and then you know you're not cured. Focusing on being cured is like hoping the other shoe won't drop. Being healed is quite different–for it refers to the process of living fully each day... being empowered to feel joy in the day-to-day processes of living... living hopefully, without knowing whether or not you've been cured."

— Candace Anderson

As we walked this new path to healing, finding our way back to living fully and mom letting herself take pleasure in the joy of living, self-care became an important focus in our lives. For mom, it was finding balance between not living in the constant shadow of cancer yet keeping health and self-care a priority. I remember her looking for ways to keep her immune system strong.

Enter "forest bathing." It was from Margaret Koch, Executive Director of the Virginia Thurston Healing Garden, that mom first heard of forest bathing. Mom started reading about forest bathing and how being under the forest canopy boosts Natural Killer (NK) cells, a type of white blood cell, in human immune systems. That was in April of 2015 and a month later, mom flew to North Carolina to train as a Certified Forest Therapy Guide with the Association of Nature and Forest Therapy Guides and Programs. That was the beginning of many new things for us, and also when mom realized I was a forest bathing mentor.

This book came about because mom and I love to be in the forest together. Pure and simple. Through trial and error, a few adjustments and patience, we found our way to forest bathing together.  We developed the techniques in this book to help other dog lovers (and even non-dog owners) add forest bathing into their walks. As any dog will tell you, please feel free to modify any of the things in this book in any way that appeals to you. They are not assignments. Make them your own. How ever you do them will be exactly the right way. We are genuinely excited to share this book with the many dog lovers out there. Imagine my tail, and whole back end for that matter, wagging with joyful exuberance.

Enjoy!

## Section 1

## What is Forest Bathing?

*"...let the soft animal of your body love what it loves..."*
-- Mary Oliver, Wild Geese

*Nadine's Reflections:*

I'm standing here on the edge of a meadow with the forest at my back thinking about this quote from Mary Oliver's poem Wild Geese. "Let the soft animal of [my] body love what it loves," and I'm asking myself, "what am I noticing?" How am I experiencing this place where the forest meets the meadow with the soft animal of **my** body? The rich scents and gentle sounds of this early afternoon in late summer are keeping me company as the touch of the breeze and sun fall pleasurably on my skin like a soft, comforting caress. I feel an urge to greet and stand among the almost head-high, late-summer flowers of yellow goldenrod and purplish Joe Pye weed. Should I? Should I stand among the flowers as one of them? Juliet comes along on her four paws and wades into the field following something, a scent perhaps, with the soft animal of her body. "Thank you" I say to her silently and I follow behind her as I wade into the field to greet the goldenrod and Joe Pye weed and stand among them as they, in their way, welcome me.

With words alone, it's hard to explain what forest bathing is. It is experiential and sensory, done with our senses and our intuition (which is also one of our senses). Forest bathing is simply taking in the atmosphere of the forest or any place with our senses. It is similar to the instinctive way our dogs are naturally, getting to know places and all kinds of living beings with their senses. Florence Williams, author of *The Nature Fix: Why Nature Makes Us Happier, Healthier, and More Creative*, writes:

> **"The idea with *shinrin yoku* [forest bathing], a term coined by the [Japanese] government in 1982 but inspired by ancient Shinto and Buddhist practices, is to let nature enter your body through all five senses."**

The Japanese term *shinrin yoku* translates to forest bathing or taking in the atmosphere of the forest. The style or philosophy of forest bathing I describe in this book I also like to call forest therapy. The forest bathing practice in this book is a combination of what Juliet and I developed for dog owners and rooted in the practice called forest therapy developed by the Association of Nature and Forest Therapy Guides and Programs (ANFT). Think of it in terms of a therapeutic practice such as massage therapy with healing benefits and not clinical therapy or eco-therapy which is a mental health practice. The terms *shinrin yoku*, forest bathing, and forest therapy are almost interchangeable. Almost. The term forest bathing has been popularized by the media, and I think of forest bathing as the umbrella term with a spectrum of similar but distinct practices underneath, each practice unique in certain

16

ways. Forest therapy implies a subtle difference in that the practice is taken up with an intentional goal of some type of healing writes M. Amos Clifford author of *Your Guide to Forest Bathing: Experience the Healing Power of Nature*.[1]

So, how does forest bathing differ from a hike in the woods, a nature walk, or meditation? Well, the primary focus of many naturalist walks is to educate—enjoyable and important, but very different from forest bathing. Similarly, when we take a walk or hike in the woods, the primary focus is often exercise or reaching a certain vista—also enjoyable and beneficial, but very different from forest bathing.

> **"The destination in forest bathing is "here" not "there."**
> — M. Amos Clifford

Some ask if forest bathing is similar to meditation, and although it is equally beneficial in the ways that meditation changes our brain patterns, forest bathing has a freedom and effortlessness that I personally don't find with meditation. Forest bathing is also different from most meditation I've experienced in that it invites pleasure, playfulness, or whatever is alive inside us.

People ask "How is forest bathing different from what I already do?" "How is forest bathing different from just taking a nice hike through the woods?" Melanie Choukas-Bradley, author of "The Joy of Forest Bathing: Reconnect With Wild Places & Rejuvenate Your Life" says:

"It's all about pace and awareness. On a forest bathing walk you slow way down, breathe deeply, and tune into your surroundings with all your senses. It's a very immersive experience and it's hard to describe what makes it so special. When you grow quiet and open your heart,

mind and five senses to all that's around you, it's extremely restorative. Your "to do" list and the day's headlines simply cease to exist when you're on forest bathing time. I have a hard time meditating in a room but nature helps me to achieve peace and serenity."[2]

**"In the practice of forest bathing we immerse our senses in the special qualities of the fluid, oceanic ambiance of the woodlands. We walk slowly so we can focus our senses on the myriad ways the living forest surrounds and touches us."**

— M. Amos Clifford

Juliet reminds me to use my senses when we are in the forest. I watch her and I am reminded to smell, listen, look, touch, and even taste. Juliet is also a master of using her intuition, her sixth sense, and I am reminded that I, too, still have the ability to sense this way. We humans actually do the bulk of our computing with our unconscious.[3] Sharon Franquemont author of *"Intuition: Your Electric Self: Creating a Life Path of Illumination"* writes:

"Intuition is a sense, just like sight or smell, a perception that brings you information. It comes to you as a still, small voice, an instinctive action, a flash of creativity, or a moment when you are one with the world. You suddenly know something without the use of analytical processes; the knowledge is just there."

Imagine for a moment you are a dog slowly strolling down a woodland trail. You have four bare paws on the ground and your nose, a few inches above the forest floor, is filled with the soft woodland scents that are much more alive lower to the ground. Your ears are relaxed but constantly adjusting as they tune in to the rhythms and story of the sounds around you. Your body is filled with the sensations and a knowing that only your senses can bring you. You are bathing in the atmosphere of the forest: alive, curious, noticing, resting, perhaps playing. You become a part of the forest. On the next pages, Juliet is inviting you on a walk to share a bit of forest bathing with you. Put on your hat and coat, and Juliet will grab the leash.

*In Juliet's Words*
**A Moment of Forest Bathing**

Mom and I were out for a morning walk and as we entered the woods, mom's attention was drawn to a small pine tree covered with sparkles. Mom is always getting distracted like this. The sparkles weren't anything that a person had done and certainly not another dog. It was the low morning sun glinting off the frozen rain and snow that fell the night before. There were neat piles of icy snow on each bunch of pine needles and frozen drops of rain on their delicate tips. All this suspended in time, glimmering in the warm morning light. We paused and mom was smiling, taking it all in, and caught up in nature's display. I tugged at mom's end of the leash giving her the signal it was time to move on. Mom is an obedient and well-behaved dog-parent, so she did as I asked without any fuss.

As we proceeded into the woods under the forest canopy, we were both feeling the excitement of being out after a fresh snow. Branches and rocks were slick with a shiny coating of ice and there were sparkles all around. The forest was singing visually and with the sound of frozen raindrops thawing and falling to the earth as the morning sun warmed them—plink, plink, plink-plink.

The air was cold but smelled wet and alive. Mom and I inhaled deeply and smiled at each other by squinting our eyes. I sniffed and uncovered a stick that promptly invited me to chew on it. Mom ate a frozen raindrop off the end of a pine needle and said it tasted like the forest.

We both looked around, up, down, far away and up close, noticing all the sparkles. Mom was smiling and looking a bit awe-struck as we wandered slowly on the trail and I kept my eye on her. We noticed the smooth trunk of a young tree covered with a thin sheen of ice. In the morning sun, the icy coating was melting and disappearing before our eyes. I paused and licked the newly melted water that puddled at the roots. It was a bit sweet like the sap from the maple tree in our backyard, and I drank some more. Mom took the opportunity to taste some more frozen raindrops from another pine tree.

We wandered on slowly, each taking turns to stop and investigate things. Before I could hear the sound of the water, I could sense moisture and coolness in the air as we approached a small stream that crosses our trail. We stepped out onto a big flat stepping-stone in the middle of the stream and stopped. The sound of the gurgling water was soothing, and we just stood for a while noticing what it was like to be in the middle of this stream. This spot had a good feeling. The water in the stream was melt-water from the hill to our left and as it passed the stone we were standing on, I wondered where it was going. As we wandered on, we were both feeling playful. Mom was feeling the joy of the morning and started humming a tune. I had a distinct spring in my step and was delighting in all the wonderful scents I was noticing. We had only gone about 50 yards.

That's a glimpse of forest bathing. Perhaps it's something you've been doing to some degree. Forest bathing turns things up a notch by putting sensory connection first.

*Slow down or pause a bit more than usual, use all of your senses to notice the forest.*

As I shift to using my senses in the forest, I notice that the forest has senses of its own. It is a community, which has sentients. Sentience, a word commonly confused with sapient or conscious, sentient means "having senses; capable of sensing" or a sentient being is capable of experiencing things through its senses. (Source: urbandictionary.com). A "sentient" being is one who perceives and responds to sensations of whatever kind: sight, hearing, touch, taste, smell or intuition. (Source: merriam-webster.com)

Plants and trees have an amazing array of very highly developed senses of their own. Plant neurobiologist, Daniel Chamovitz, and author of *"What a plant Knows: A field guide to the senses"* writes:

> "Plants are acutely aware of the world around them. They are aware of their visual environment; they differentiate between red, blue, far red, and UV lights and respond accordingly. They are aware of aromas surrounding them and respond to minute quantities of volatile compounds wafting in the air. Plants know when they are being touched and can distinguish different touches. They are aware of gravity: they can change their shapes to ensure that shoots grow up and roots grow down. And plants are aware of their past: they remember past infections and the conditions they've weathered and then modify their current physiology based on these memories."

The sense of community with the forest that I have developed personally through forest bathing is very palpable to me. This is a community where I can just be. I have a sense of the forest community both as a whole and as individual beings: trees, plants, creatures, streams, and even places. Author Peter Wohlleben shares these facts about the communities that trees form with each other and as a forest community in *"The Hidden Life of Trees: What They Feel, How They Communicate—Discoveries from A Secret World."*

"We have learned that mother trees recognize and talk with their kin, shaping future generations. In addition, injured trees pass their legacies on to their neighbors, affecting gene regulation, defense chemistry, and resilience in the forest community."

"But the most astonishing thing about trees is how social they are. The trees in a forest care for each other, sometimes even going so far as to nourish the stump of a felled tree for centuries after it was cut down by feeding it sugars and other nutrients, and so keeping it alive. Only some stumps are thus nourished. Perhaps they are the parents of the trees that make up the forest of today. A tree's most important means of staying connected to other trees is a "wood wide web" of soil fungi that connects vegetation in an intimate network that allows the sharing of an enormous amount of information and goods. Scientific research aimed at understanding the astonishing abilities of this partnership between fungi and plant has only just begun. The reason trees share food and communicate is that they need each other. It takes a forest to create a microclimate suitable for tree growth and sustenance. So, it's not surprising that isolated trees have far shorter lives than those living connected together in forests."

## Tending and Being Tended by the Land

The forest is offering you an invitation. Be it pleasure or something that boosts your sense of well-being, health or healing. Let your relationship to the land deepen. Whether it be in your garden, your front stoop, the forest, the ocean or all of the above, open your senses and begin to notice your sense of place or relationship to the land with your body. "Let the soft animal of your body love what it loves [4]"

I ask, "How am I tended by my relationship with the forest?" or "How does the forest tend me?" Have you ever asked yourself those questions? Why are we often so hesitant to talk about having a relationship with the land, the forest, or trees? We are all living beings after all. The passage below from *"Braiding Sweetgrass: Indigenous Wisdom, Scientific Knowledge and the Teachings of Plants"* by Robin Wall Kimmerer, gets at the "elephant in the room."

> "I sat once in a graduate writing workshop on relationships to the land. The students all demonstrated a deep respect and affection for nature. They said that nature was the place where they experienced the greatest sense of belonging and well-being. They professed without reservation that they loved the earth. And then I asked them, 'Do you think that the earth loves you back?' No one was willing to answer that. So, I made it hypothetical and asked, 'What do you suppose would happen if people believed this crazy notion that the earth loved them back?' The floodgates opened. They all wanted to talk at once. We were suddenly off the deep end, heading for world peace and perfect harmony. Knowing that you love the earth changes you, activates you to defend and protect and celebrate. But when

you feel that the earth loves you in return, that feeling transforms the relationship from a one-way street into a sacred bond."

As I explore my own relationship with the forest, I ask, "How does the earth love me? Where and how do I feel this connection in my own body, with my own intuition?" For me, it is in a soft heart. It is simply that the earth and all its beings share their gifts with me. I find myself wanting to reciprocate and thinking about how to reciprocate appropriately. We each have to find our own authentic way with this, and for me, it is the act of tending the land in small ways for the tending I receive. We are sharing our gifts with each other. For me, it can be as simple as picking up trash or introducing new people to the forest in the way of forest bathing on guided walks or workshops. The tending I receive can be simple pleasures along the trail or the feeling of knowing that I am part of the community that makes up all the living beings of the forest. It is through feeling my relationship with the land itself.

We all have many simple ways of sharing and tending each other. You will find your ways if you don't already know them. Perhaps ask the forest and wait for them to emerge. Juliet and I exchange gifts all the time. Mentor that she is, Juliet rolls over and offers me the gift of her belly to rub, which makes me smile and my heart go soft. I return the gift by rubbing her belly, of course. I smile and we both are sensing the pleasure it brings us to exchange our gifts. It doesn't need to be complicated.

*In Juliet's Words*
I am a dog.
Things are simple for me.
I do not doubt that the earth loves me.

# Take it to the Forest

## What is Forest Bathing?

Consider the following:

- Notice scents and sounds as you walk.
- Take instinctive opportunities to slow down and pause as your dog pauses along the trail.
- Watch the senses your dog uses most.
- Which of your other senses do you feel drawn to most?
- What is your intuition or sixth sense telling you?
- Try using all of your senses, not just your sight, to keep track of your dog.
- After being in the forest, what are you noticing about how the forest is tending you?
- Is there a way you might like to tend the land in return?
- Each of us has our own unique way of relating to the forest. What might yours be?
- Forest bathing/forest therapy is a practice that deepens over time.

# Section 2

## Forest Bathing with Your Dog:
## Key Tips

*Nadine's Reflections:*

It's June 2015, and I've just arrived back home from North Carolina where I trained to become a Certified Forest Therapy Guide. My heart and mind are full with the joy of my heightened senses and feeling the community of the forest. Although Juliet and I have been exploring the woods together for years, today was the first time I was aware of her offering me a forest bathing invitation and made a conscious choice to accept.

The morning is a perfect temperature for short sleeves and the air has a quality of being soft and fragrant with the rich scents of the forest floor. Juliet and I come around a bend in the gently, rolling trail and ahead of us the forest floor is covered with knee-high, bright green, waving ferns. Dappled sunlight breaks through the treetops, lands on the ferns, and they seem even more animated. I can't help but smile in my pleasure of the ferns and I feel myself drawn to them. "Come play," they seem to be calling to me. Juliet hears something and wades into the ferns to explore. And I realize this was my invitation from Juliet. Just follow Juliet's lead, I reminded myself. There was a moment of saying to myself, "Oh, that's silly, wading in among the ferns with your dog." But I set the thought aside and instead listened to my heart. I stepped in among the ferns and it was so much fun. Wading among the waving ferns and dappled sunlight. Smelling the scents released by feet and movement. Touching their leaf tips with my fingertips. Noticing the two worlds, the one below the fern fronds where my feet were and the one above where the rest of me was. So delicate and full of playfulness. So enjoyable! Later I wrote about our walk that morning. It still makes me smile.

> "We played in a field of lush, green ferns looking for chipmunks;
> we discovered a giant old pine tree with a secret animal house in it;
> we followed a sunlit path and turned around when we heard cars;
> we heard something deep in the woods and tried to find it."

This notion of being invited by both our dogs and the forest is one I have come to really love. It's so simple. Our dogs are guiding us by example and in doing so, inviting us to use our own senses to engage with the forest and our surroundings.

But the idea of forest bathing with a dog may also seem problematic. How can you slow down and notice things when your dog is tugging on the leash or running in the woods? Rather than try to change these realities, work with them. It's easier than you might think. Although this book is a guide, it is not

32

about how to train your dog. Rather Juliet and I share our way of being in the forest while forest bathing. I'll break things down, share seven pointers, and direct you to training resources that will bring some ease to the practice of forest bathing with your dog.

## 1) Our Dogs' Natural Way

First on the list is tapping into our dogs' natural way of being and working with that to have them work with us. Humans and dogs have a very unique bond. I don't need to tell you this, but naming this connection helps to highlight one of the most important points of this book. We can sense each other's mood and energy and we take intuitive cues from each other more than any other animal-human pairing [or even human-human pairing]. This makes us great forest bathing partners.

Dogs have superior ability to read human signals and pick up subtle social cues. They have the ability to read human body language and are also tuned to respond to the emotional state of both their fellow canines and that of their humans. Our dogs sense that our movements and gestures contain important cues as to what will happen next. All social mammals have evolved ways of reading the subtle signals they send to other members of the same species, but dogs can also read certain types of social cues in humans in addition to their own species. Here is an amazing fact: Dogs and puppies can interpret body language signals from humans four times better than apes and more than twice as well as young children.[5]

**Trust in your dog's ability to learn and read your unspoken cues**

Tapping into our dogs' talent to read our unspoken cues is one of the secrets to forest bathing with your dog. The reverse is also true. When our dogs are with us, "forest bathing moments" are ours for the taking. Tune in to your dog's way of being in the forest. They are masters at inviting us to enter the sensory zone. For example, who among us doesn't love to watch our dogs in their element, playing, running, investigating, or enjoying a good chew on a stick or toy? They are so in the moment using their canine senses to take it all in. I am so filled with joy when I watch Juliet run and play or even just enjoy the simple pleasure of chewing on a good stick. Watching our dogs do what they love, we are brought into our senses and experience that same sense of joy.

> "We live in a high-tech, low-touch world and people have a longing for a bond with nature." Companion animals like dogs can be that bond."

> "...these bonds help us to feel good. ... When we see, touch, hear or talk to our [dogs], beneficial neurohormones are released and that induces a sense of goodwill, joy, nurturing and happiness. At the same time, the stress hormone cortisol is suppressed. Heart rate, blood pressure and respiratory rate can all decrease, leaving us more relaxed and able to manage stress in ways that aren't harmful to our health."[6]

**Take-Aways:**

1. Trust in your dog's ability to learn and read your unspoken cues.
2. Notice your dog's way of being in the sensory zone.
3. Start to notice and read the cues your dog is sharing with you.

## 2) A Long Leash and Off-Leash

*In Juliet's Words*
On Leashes: Mom tends to get distracted and wander off. If I'm totally honest, I tend to wander myself and can't refuse following a fresh scent trail deep into the forest or chasing a squirrel up a tree. Mom says, "Our first responsibility is to keep each other safe," so I keep track of her with a 20-foot training lead. This works really well for us. This longer lead gives us each some space to stop and sniff or wander ahead without constantly tugging on each other.

On-Leash vs. Off-Leash: Safety First! Our first responsibility is to each other and those who care about us to be safe and stay found. Keep track of each other, where you are and what is around you. You don't have to be off-leash when forest bathing and if you do, go off-leash only when it is safe for everyone: you, your dog, and wildlife.

Is a leash necessary or helpful? It is for me and Juliet and it totally depends on your individual situation. We have our off-leash times, but when we are in the woods or sitting for a while somewhere, we use a 20-foot training lead. This longer lead gives us each some space to stop and sniff or walk on without constantly tugging on each other. TIP: You can clip two leashes together to make one longer one. On the other hand, if your dog is off-leash try using more than just your sense of sight to help you keep track of him/her. Clip a bell on his collar for added ease. Experiment with listening and even sensing with your intuition in addition to doing visual checks. Where do you sense they are? What are they telling you?

Think through your situation and do what is right for you and your dog. You don't want to lose track of each other. Do you and your dog stick close together off-leash or are you like Juliet and myself who both tend to wander off following our curiosity? You are seeking a balance of freedom to explore and move ahead or pause as you walk together or sit a while.

Nora the Newfoundland who lives next-door is getting on in her years and is content to stay close to her dad when they walk in the woods. On the other hand, Sparky and Ellie are two younger golden retrievers who live down the street. They will roam far and wide if their mom doesn't keep an eye on them, and of course, two dogs are just more to keep track of than one. What is the best way to work in some forest bathing moments to your walk with two off-leash dogs? Don't fight the natural flow. Let everyone get their energy out first. Take advantage of the natural pauses that our dogs create for us along the trail, and if a place to sit presents itself at the end of your walk, take it. More on pausing and sitting with our dogs is next.

## Wildlife and Your Dog

Some dogs chase wildlife. They are dogs after all and it is their natural instinct to hunt and kill prey. In the winter and spring in particular, wildlife is put at risk when disturbed. In winter, the mere act of being chased from a roost can cost an animal valuable energy reserves and perhaps even its life. In the spring, being chased can separate parents and babies. These are delicate times of year for wildlife. Be thoughtful about the possibilities of our off-leash dogs disturbing wildlife. Letting our dogs off-leash can be awesome, but consider the time of year and where. Know the land, its rules, including hunting or trapping policies and its inhabitants.

**Take-Aways:**

1. Safety first!
2. Recommended: Twenty-foot nylon training lead (cotton is good, too, but is heavier and collects more dirt).
3. Don't fight the natural flow and take advantage of the natural pauses.

## 3) Taking Advantage of Natural Pauses—"Paws" with Your Dog

Forest bathing can be part of your walk and not necessarily the only thing you do. When I'm out with Juliet, we are both exercising and finding some moments for forest bathing along our way. Sometimes they are very short pauses, and other times, we sit for a time or wander slowly for a while. Making room during your walks for a bit of everything creates ease.

Noticing the natural transitions of pauses and slowing down or speeding up as you walk along the trail is key. Pausing when our dog pauses is perhaps the most natural forest bathing thing we can do along the trail. When I first go outside, there's an instinct to pause and see what's going on. Juliet does the same. She looks around and gets an overall sense of what's happening. Next, she pauses and checks things out in a closer way sniffing or leaving her own scent. Noticing these transitional moments and taking advantage of them for forest bathing is a natural fit. Step outside and get a sense of the day with your own senses just as your dog is doing. As you move along and your dog pauses, pause with him/her to notice what might be going on in that spot along the trail. For example, you may notice something you are drawn to, like a spot of sunlight on a rock through the trees, some soft, green moss that beckons you to touch it, or even the old log your dog is noticing or how he/she is sniffing and investigating with deep satisfaction and intensity. Just let yourself notice things and be drawn to whatever is calling you. If there is pleasure or curiosity in what you are noticing, give that hospitality in whatever way feels right. Simply noticing and enjoying the pleasure. As you make space for these pauses, this practice becomes more and more natural.

I used to be impatient waiting for Juliet to finish sniffing something or taking a bathroom break. Now I use it as an opportunity for the simple pleasures of forest bathing. While we have our times when we need to walk on or Juliet is heeling, we also have free times when stopping to sniff is okay. Rather than rushing through these moments, they are a welcomed opportunity to pause myself and look around, listen, touch, smell, and simply be in that spot. Remember the old saying "Stop and smell the roses?" Pausing is a chance to notice what is happening here, now, in this spot. How much or long should dogs sniff? Veterinarian Pete Wedderburn, BVM&S CertVR MRCVS [7], shares some great analogies in his article "How Long Should a Dog Take Sniffing on a Walk?"

> "How long should someone be left to look at a picture in an art gallery before being asked to move along? The answer is as long as they want to keep looking.' For as long as they continue to gaze at the picture, they are obviously enjoying the sight of the work of art. And how long should someone be left listening to a song? The answer is 'as long as they want to keep listening.' Nobody wants to have the radio turned off in the middle of an enjoyable piece of music [and be

7 Bachelor of Veterinary Medicine & Surgery (University of Edinburgh, Scotland), Certificate in Veterinary Radiology, Member of Royal College of Veterinary Surgeons

dragged away] while they are still appreciating the sound. And so it is for dogs sniffing in undergrowth. Give them as long as they want. Wrap up warmly so that you don't mind waiting around, and let them have a drawn-out, lengthy, indulgent, deep inhalation. It's one of their favorite pastimes, so don't rush them off. Take a long pause, and let them enjoy those sniffing sensations.'"[8]

Alexandra Horowitz, author of *Inside of a Dog: What Dogs See, Smell, and Know* says,

**"I always recommend that one walk a day be a smell walk. (...) It takes a little patience but (…) it became rewarding to me, too, when I started seeing how much fun it was for him. Instead of just yanking him to get around the block quickly ."**

What if you were actually inviting pauses the way you would wander through a museum? What is the music or art I am noticing as Juliet and I wander down the trail? Here are examples of some things I've noticed just pausing with Juliet along the trail.

- A spot of sunlight through the trees highlighting a spot on the forest floor.
- A pairing of rocks and green moss.
- A puddle by the side of the trail reflecting the sky.
- The shadow of a fern in the morning sun.

What if you were actually inviting pauses along your walking trail recognizing them as opportunities for forest bathing moments? Remember,

there is no one way to do forest bathing. Allow the ebb and flow as you walk down the trail, pausing along the way. I call this "forest bathing in a minute."

**"Forest bathing can be more like a dance.**
**Like the ocean tide ebbing and flowing rhythmically as it changes.**
— M. Amos Clifford

While forest bathing with your dog often comes in little snippets and pauses, it can also be for an extended time. It really depends on your dog, the day, how much time you have, your intentions for the combination of relaxing walk or exercise you desire on that day, etc. The most important thing is to be open to what is inviting you.

**Take-Aways:**

1. Slow down and pause with your dog.
2. Look around until something catches your eye when your dog pauses.
3. Let your dog enjoy a good long sniff whenever possible.

## 4) Teaching Your Dog the Art of Relaxed Forest-Sitting

Relaxed sitting in the forest is something Juliet and I do often, but getting her to relax is not always easy. I should also say that although I am using the term "relaxed forest-sitting," I am using it to refer to anything from sitting or lying to just hanging out in a relaxed, quiet way. In the next few pages, I'll share the way I approached this with Juliet, but know that there is more than one way to approach this with your dog. Find what will work best for you.

**One: Our approach**

Although Juliet is a good dog and knows various cues, she doesn't do them for an extended time. It is also my style that I don't want to be monitoring her when we're sitting in the woods, so we took a more holistic approach that incorporates Juliet's natural way of being in the forest and her natural ability to read me. This approach felt more organic, and if I'm honest, it also took time and patience. I am allowing Juliet to figure out what I want through modeling it myself and giving her space to mirror my behavior in her own way. I had to trust that the influence of my own energy and behavior would cue Juliet. I also needed to be patient for her to come around on her own in her own time. When I become quiet, Juliet often does, too. Remember that our dogs have the ability to read human signals and pick up subtle social cues. Trust in that. Allow time for your dog to read and mirror you in their own authentic way. Be patient here.

## Two: Evaluating your spot together

When I first sit down, I allow us both time to check out our spot. For me this doesn't take long (a moment or two). I've already done some of this "scouting" visually as we approach the spot and before I even sit. Juliet is different. She needs a bit longer to check out our selected space and to be able to "scout the spot" in the way dogs do, mostly through scent and by tasting a few things. This is especially true if it is a new spot. This is part of our process of settling in to sit, and I allow time for Juliet to smell and explore the immediate area and be comfortable in her surroundings. It can be a few minutes or more than ten or fifteen minutes. My fellow Certified Forest Therapy Guide and Educator and student of Positive Reinforcement Training, Sue Schiemer, says "Dogs use all their senses to evaluate potential threats and determine what's going on—is there a threat or is it safe?" People do the same thing, but in our own way, using different senses and at a different speed than dogs. I wouldn't want someone to lead me to a spot in the woods and tell me to sit without being able to first look around and see what's there, would you? We shouldn't ask our dogs to do that either. After all, isn't exploring a new spot with our senses also what forest bathing is all about?

> Let them sense where you are putting your attention.

## Three: Be patient

Allow your dog their "natural way" and trust that they will follow your lead when they are ready. Older dogs will be ready sooner than

younger dogs, and on some days your dog may not settle at all. After a time of looking over our spot and likely chewing on a few sticks or digging a hole, or all of the above, Juliet usually notices that my attention is focused on watching the forest and she settles down and starts watching too. (If your dog doesn't chew sticks you could bring a chew toy or Kong filled with frozen peanut butter as another option.) Sometimes Juliet doesn't settle for long and fusses or whines. Don't give up if your dog doesn't settle quickly. It's just like working with a child. You have to show your resolve. Let them sense where you are putting your attention. Your dog may settle down to sit in one attempt or more likely, it may take practice over months as your dog realizes what you are expecting of them. For this reason, having a verbal cue like "settle" that lets Juliet know what I want can be helpful on the days that I need it. Most of the time, I let Juliet naturally settle without any verbal cues from me. You'll need to experiment and find what is best for you and your dog.

Don't automatically assume you need the "settle" cue. After making sure everyone's needs are met, see if your dog can pick up your energy and settle down on their own. If you are relaxed, they will likely be, too. If you are restless and looking at your phone, they will be restless as well.

**Four: Checking for stress**

I do want to briefly mention that if your dog is restless, be aware if they are moving from restlessness into anxiety or stress. If your dog is feeling stress because they are not sure what to do, then teaching them the "settle" cue can really help. There may also be another cause for the stress like cold, so fully assess the situation. Just as you might need something to sit on to prevent your bum from getting too cold so might your dog. Your dog may also just be restless and want their way. If you sense it is restlessness, you can experiment with sitting through it and slowly increasing the time over days. If you determine your dog is stressing, keep the sitting session short. Wait for them to have a few seconds of calm sitting and then reward them by getting up and moving on for the day. Sue Schiemer also suggests that when we catch our dogs relaxing and settling on their own, giving them a reinforcer (treat or affection, etc.) can be a great touch. Be sure not to leave immediately after your dog has whined or barked as that will reinforce that unwanted behavior. Our dogs are masters at training us to do what they want. Rather, wait for several seconds of quiet calm, and then reward that by moving on.

**Five: Some tips for relaxed forest-sitting**

1. Save the sitting for the end of a walk when your pup (and you) have burned off most of your energy.

2. There are going to be days when neither you nor your dog settle, and that's likely for some good reason such as a chipmunk runs under your noses. Perhaps that's a clue to pay attention to that or be invited into that exploration or adventure.

3. Your dog knows if you pull out your phone. They can sense the change in focus and often become restless.

4. Try looping the long leash on something nearby so your dog can do their

thing without tugging on you and you are still keeping track of each other.

5. Juliet has also learned to offer me a sit at various places along the trail. I plan for this, and if we have the time, I almost always accept her invitation to sit. Some days there is time for this and other days one of us has to get to the office.

6. Finding a spot to sit or stand: You may even have a spot already in mind, but if you don't, wander until you feel a pull to a spot. It may be subtle or strong.

7. Allow yourself to find another spot if the first one doesn't feel right.

8. This is not an assignment or a meditation. "Simply choose a place to sit and… be."[9] Let the forest recalibrate to its rhythms. Be still and quiet. You'll become part of the forest and it will become a part of you.

9. Let your dog also explore this spot in their way, by sniffing everything, so they feel comfortable enough to relax. (See Relaxed Forest Sitting in section 2.) A cue to settle may be helpful if your dog is becoming more fidgety or even anxious. Don't give a cue too soon, however. Allow them space to sniff, explore and use their senses first. And don't expect your dog to settle if you yourself are still fidgety or looking at your phone. You must set an authentic example for your dog to follow.

10. See the resources section at the back of this book for some additional settling options

**Six: It starts to become automatic**

Months later after we first started this process, Juliet now knows some

of the spots we sit and she settles down even before I do. Don't give up. Over time, we've both come to enjoy relaxed forest-sitting and watching. Once Juliet understood what we were doing and what I wanted, it got much easier. There are times when I'm ready to go and she still wants to sit and watch. We have spots that we frequent and she knows now that when we come to one of our spots, we will just relax and settle in. There was a time I thought Juliet would never learn to settle down and just sit, but in time she did. What I'm trying to say is don't give up. When your dog fusses, let them fuss. They'll settle down after a bit. It can take time to create new routines. Keep at it.

**Take-Aways:**

1. Have patience. It may take weeks or months to develop this sitting or settling practice.

2. Start with a few minutes and slowly build up the length of time you sit.

3. Be authentic in allowing yourself to relax and settle in. If you're not, your dog will know.

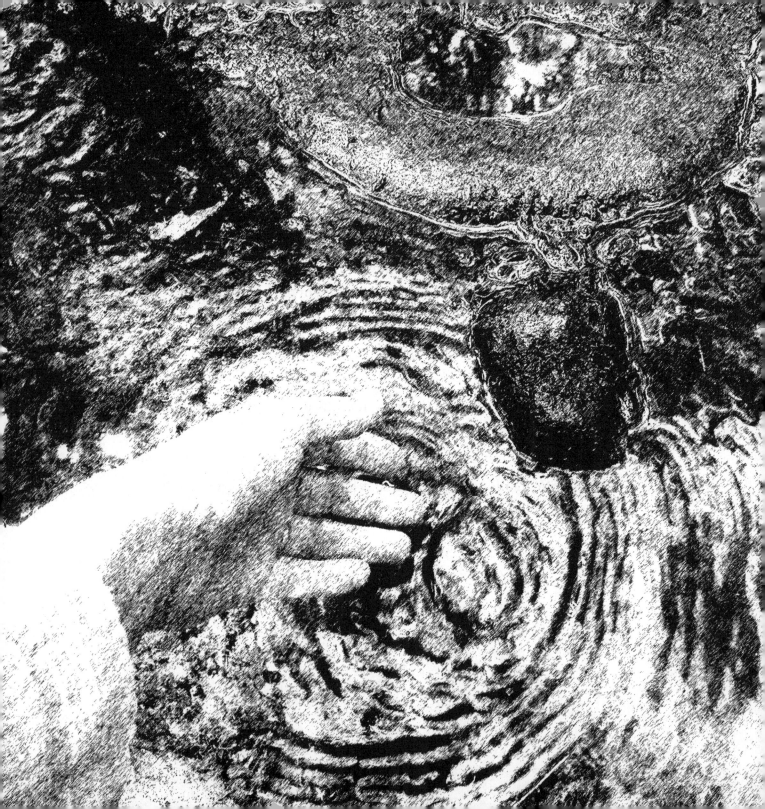

*In Juliet's Words*

**A Moment of Sitting in the Forest**

Mom and I were on the banks of a small stream just off the trail. One of our favorite places to sit. There was always lots to notice and enjoy by this stream. I waded in the water and enjoyed the cool mud squishing between the pads of my paws. The decaying leaves smelled rich and earthy. I drank a bit of the muddy water from the stream's edge and looked around. I especially love drinking from the edge where it's a bit muddy. The water always has more flavor there. Mom was sitting on a rock watching a miniature waterfall flow under a fallen log. The sun was warming the leaves on the ground. Mom smiled and said aloud to nobody in particular, "Can you smell the sunshine on the leaves?" We sat, allowing time and space to take in the feel and smell of the sun. Simultaneously, we stretched, took a deep breath, and then exhaled.

The leaves on the trees were just emerging and it looked like there were tiny green butterflies everywhere. The sounds of the stream were a quiet gurgle as the spring melt water seeped out of the ground and followed its path gently through the rocks. A small bird landed downstream and was taking a bath. My ears perked and my attention sharpened—just a bit—and then relaxed again. Mom noticed the bird, too. She had been watching the reflection of the trees on the water's surface, but now she was picking up pebbles and started playfully making a design with some of the pebbles from the stream on top of a rock. We both just sat quietly, watching the happenings in the forest and following whatever drew our attention. The forest and its rhythms went on—only we were now part of the forest too. After a while, we both stirred again. I looked up and squeezed my eyes at mom. Mom smiled back and squeezed her eyes in return. There was a familiar wonderful sense of belonging here in the forest. We both felt it.

## 5) Wandering, or Sauntering, as Henry David Thoreau Would Call It

**"I have met with but one or two persons in the course of my life who have understood the art of Walking, that is, of taking walks, who had a genius, so to speak, for sauntering."**

— Henry David Thoreau

Thoreau seems to catch our attention with the directness of his declaration "the art of walking." This resonates with me as forest bathing is a practice that seems similarly simple on the surface, but there is so much more if one slows down and looks deeper. I interpret Thoreau's reflections as: be open and without agenda to be here, now and not over there in the future or past; receive the gifts from nature that are offered along the way; follow your curiosity and pleasure; take your time and be here. In our fast-paced lives today, the ability to allow ourselves to saunter, unwinding naturally, is both a joy and very beneficial.

Often, we're walking fast in the forest, hiking and getting exercise. Let me be clear, there is no need to stop that. Instead, add some moments here and there to wander or sit and bathe yourself in the atmosphere of the forest. I don't fight the natural flow of our routine doing exercise and such. However, I am also alert to when natural breaks, both short and long, present themselves, and I accept these "invitations" from Juliet and the forest to pause. Thoreau said, "It's a great art to saunter." Saun·ter: to walk in a slow, relaxed manner, without hurry or effort; a leisurely stroll, amble, wander, meander, drift, take the air.[10]

Allow yourself to experiment with varying your pace. You don't have to only wander slowly. Go fast, hike, run, get your exercise and at some point, pause or sit for a bit. Do both. If your thing isn't to sit at all then, just keep moving and greet the forest as you glide by. My guess is that at some point you will naturally pause and rest. Notice how your dog moves down the trail: wandering—pausing—running—pausing—wandering. Allow the forest and your dog to offer you this natural invitation to pause and observe. I find that I tend to walk first and at some point, the forest invites me to sit. I just need to listen to the soft animal of my body.[11]

What might this look like? Here are a few ideas, but it could be any combination of these things.

- Hike and use a log or rock for a spot to sit along the trail.
- Exercise and afterward sit on a park bench.
- Take a walk and sit in your yard or next to your front door when you get home and just notice what's going on around you in this space.
- Work in your garden, and at some point, pause for longer than your usual 5-10 or even 20 minutes and just notice what it's like to be one of the plant or animal beings that live or spend time in this garden.

**Take-Aways:**

1. Look for natural breaks during your hike, exercise or walk.

2. Try wandering companionably in silence for a time when walking with friends and family.

3. Saunter like Thoreau. Slow down sometimes. It's amazing what more there is to notice.

## 6) "Yeah, But *My* Dog..." - Special Circumstances and Awarnesses

After reading this, are you still saying, "Yeah, but my dog..." or perhaps, "How much do I try to control or direct my dog during forest bathing?" While it's not possible to provide solutions for all situations, it is the nature of forest bathing to take it in whatever way it comes. In other words, adapt to your situation finding your unique way with your dog. It may take some experimenting and patience. Your dog will likely be the one to suggest the solution, so pay attention to him/her. Here are a few situations and examples of how I might find my way through them.

How much do you try to control your dog during forest bathing?

1. I have a puppy: Be a puppy with your puppy.

2. My dog can't go far or lags behind: Ah, your dog is inviting you to slow down. Listen to her. Let go of needing to go far. Explore or sit down where you are.

3. Something to sit on: Have something to sit on for your dog and you. It can get chilly sitting on the ground when it's cold, especially if you have an older dog. Bring something for each of you to sit on if you plan to sit.

4. My dog is always pulling at their leash: Try using the 20-foot 'training lead'. Allow some time for both your dog and you to get used to it.

5. My dog and I are very active and like to keep moving. By all means, do what feels right for you. My guess is that at some point you will pause or take a rest and that's a natural moment to do a bit of forest bathing.

6. Whining or barking: Wait until it stops and count two to three seconds before you move on so you don't reinforce the behavior.

7. Be thoughtful about the precise moment you give corrections to your dog if you need one for safety or another situation. You may be unintentionally giving verbal (saying the word "no") or nonverbal (jerking on the leash) information that can be conflicting to your dog when allowing them to sniff and explore.

8. Adverse situations: There are all kinds of adverse situations we can encounter: wildlife, plant life, other dogs, your dog runs off, etc. If your dog is not responding effectively to voice commands and getting into tangles with or pursuing other creatures, a leash is likely in order. A 20-foot training lead in the woods offers control with lots of freedom to both of you and when you get to a safe off-leash area you can let them go.

9. You may already have an awareness of the possibility of adverse situations with other dogs if you've had a bad experience and perhaps even some fear. Some strategies to help are thoughtful about where and when you walk and avoid high risk areas at high traffic times. Pay attention to your own energy and what subliminal signals you are projecting to your dog. Step off the trail if another dog is coming that you are unsure about. Watch your dog for signs to see if they want to step off the trail. I find myself following Juliet's lead most of the time. She can tell if she doesn't have a good feeling about another dog better than I can most of the time.

10. When you catch your dog sitting and waiting without being told, giving them a reinforcer can be a great touch.

**Take-Aways:**

1. Be open to adapting.

2. Follow your dog's lead.

3. Consult a professional dog trainer when you are not sure how to handle a situation. See the resource section in the back of the book.

## 7) Getting Yourself Ready for Forest Bathing

*In Juliet's Words*

**Getting ready to go forest bathing**

As dogs, most of us tend to be free spirits and not consider the practical side of things. Now that I think about it, I don't think I have a practical bone in my dog-body. Mom, on the other hand, is very practical and knows that many of you will find it helpful if we share some things to be aware of and tips about how to get ready for forest bathing.

Things to think about or be on the lookout for:

1. **Clothing:** Forest bathing doesn't require any special equipment, but you do want to be comfortable, warm, and dry. I always wear an extra layer or two that I can take off or put back on. Gloves, hat, neck warmer, and good socks in cold weather are also a must for me, and in the winter, I often wear ski pants. I want to be able to stroll slowly and plop down to sit just about anywhere and be comfortable. Equally important in

the summer is a sun hat, water and protection from biting insects. A lightweight stool or sit-upon is also an option. In the resources section of the back of the book, we share a link to our favorite lightweight stool. I sometimes use a piece of yoga mat that folds up small and is easy to stick in my pocket to keep my bum dry when sitting. The ground is cold for our dogs too so bringing something for them to rest on should be considered as well.

2. **Phone**: Should you put your phone away? Yes. Just try it. See what it's like without your phone. How does having your phone out during a stroll compare with being phone free? Once I get past the anxiety of turning my phone off, I find I don't want to turn it back on.

3. **Photos**: To take photos or not? Today it's so easy to take a photograph and share it. We're in the habit of photographing everything, but that doesn't mean we should. Be selective about when to take a photo and when to just enjoy something. I still take photos, but more often I let the urge to take a photo pass and enjoy the moment by being fully here.

4. **Poison ivy/poison oak**: Learn to identify these plants if you have one or both in your area. Dogs aren't affected by poison ivy/poison oak, but people can pick it up from a dog's coat. It's the oily sap from these plants that people react to. As a precaution, I try to always wash my hands with soap and a washcloth when I get home because these plants can cause an itchy rash for humans that can sometimes be very serious. That said, they also have a good side. The berries of poison ivy/oak are some of the most fat-rich berries providing needed nutrition for birds, and it's a great food plant for deer and other browsers. Poison ivy also has some of the most beautiful red-orange-yellow fall foliage. If Juliet wanders

towards a patch of poison ivy, I often make a clucking sound to redirect her in another direction.

5. **Ticks**: Do lots of tick checks on yourself and your dog. Consult your vet to determine the best tick prevention strategy for your dog. For myself, I always do a tick check when I get home and toss my clothes in the dryer. "Most ticks are VERY sensitive to dryness. The very first action to take after being outside is to strip clothing off and put it in the dryer. Deer ticks are most abundant, while American dog ticks, Lone Star ticks and other Amblyomma species are more robust. To be sure that each species achieves fatal crispiness, leave clothes in the dryer on high for 10 minutes. Gas dryers get hotter than electric dryers, so you might want to add 5 minutes if you own an electric dryer. Believe it or not, ticks are not killed by washing, even in hot water. Clothing just left in the hamper or on the floor may put the next person to touch it at risk. Dry first—then wash." -- Visit tickencounter.org  for more info on preventing tick bites.

6. **Other animals and plants**: Awareness and gift. It is a joy to see wild creatures. Often people become scared and over-react. While it is a first impulse to react negatively to things that have the potential to harm us, it is also a great gift to see and be among wildlife. I personally feel full of awe when I have a moment like this. There may be animals and plants to be aware of in your area.  Pick up a guide book for your region or ask local experts for guidance on how to respond appropriately when you do have an encounter this will increase both your personal safety and your enjoyment.

**Take-Aways:**

1. Dress for warmth and comfort in hot and cold weather.

2. Know the wildlife in your area and how to respond during an encounter.

3. Do a tick check when you get home and every time you change your clothes.

4. Wash your hands with soap and a washcloth if you think you may have been exposed to poison ivy or oak.

5. Turn your cellphone off, but keep it with you.

### Equipment and Safety Checklist

- Consider harness vs. collar. Harnesses typically offer better control, reduce pulling, and can prevent injury for both your dog and you. We use a non restrictive harness.

- Consider a long training lead. We use a 20-foot nylon training lead, and it has made our walks more enjoyable for us both. Have ID tags with your name and contact information.

- Use bells if your dog is off leash so both you and wildlife can hear where he/she is.

- GPS: We use a small device called Whistle.

- Know the leash laws.

- Know the land: Is hunting or trapping permitted? When are the different hunting seasons?

- Using a hands-free leash attachment can be helpful.

- Carrying a first aid kit on hikes and longer walks is a smart idea.

## "Take it to the Forest"

### Forest Bathing with Your Dog

- Tune in to your dog's natural way of being and use that as a guide.
- Use a long lead that gives you and your dog space to stop and sniff or wander on without constantly tugging on each other.
- Notice the natural pauses along the trail.
- Let the urge to check your phone or take a picture pass.
- Practice the art of sauntering.
- Dress for comfort and warmth.

# Section 3

## Forest Bathing is Restorative for Our Dogs

*In Juliet's Words*
**Anxiety and Forest Bathing**

I am a dog who does not like loud noises. Many noises make me nervous and lead to an anxiety attack which is no fun at all. I get stressed-out rather easily, if I'm honest. Being in the forest, following the scent trails, engaging all of my senses calms my anxiety. Suddenly I'm relaxed, my tail is swinging gently, and my nerves are calm. I feel restored to my own self.

Modern life can be just as stressful for dogs as it is for humans. These days, the sympathetic nervous system of our dogs (responsible for the fight-or-flight response) is often in a constant state of low-grade activation with periodic huge spikes. This constant low-grade activation of our sympathetic nervous system over time is what wreaks the most havoc on our bodies and minds. What is missing in modern life is an effective way to activate the relaxation response. Activating the relaxation response engages the parasympathetic nervous system responsible for the rest-and-digest state that allows a body to recover and heal. For dogs and humans, engaging in sensory activities such as forest bathing activates the relaxation response thereby reducing stress and anxiety naturally and effectively.[12]

**"The more dogs engage with their surroundings, the more stress gets reduced."**

— Karen Marsh, Canine Behaviorist

While there is a lot of research that supports the sensory-nature-wellbeing connection, this fact is also evident through the anecdotal evidence of simply observing the changes in our dogs and ourselves. How do you feel when you come back from a walk? What before and after changes do you notice in your dog?

**"Every dog needs to sniff, investigate and forage. It seems to make them feel whole."**

— Ali Brown, M.Ed., CPDT-KA, CDBC,[13] author of
*Scaredy Dog! Understanding & Rehabilitating Your Reactive Dog*

**"Our dogs are intelligent and impulsive—both of which can get them in trouble in human society. Forest bathing helps dogs (and people) cope and keep their sanity in check."**

— Sue Schiemer, Certified Forest Therapy Guide,
Educator and Student of Positive Reinforcement Training

The sensory engagement that is an essential part of forest bathing is also directly linked to the health, healing, and well-being of our dogs. Sue goes on to say that forest bathing is an experience that is reflective of and meets the

---

13 Certified Professional Dog Trainer-Knowledge Assessed (CPDT-KA) , Certified Dog Behavior Consultant (CDBC)

needs of our dogs. By meeting the needs for the dogs we love, we will be able to meet in the center ring of the Venn diagram, garnering benefits for our dogs, ourselves and the forest.

The sense of smell is especially important for our dogs. When our dogs are born, it's their sense of smell that first guides them to their mother's milk. Interestingly, this is also the same for human babies who can smell their mother's milk and intuitively work their way towards the source to nurse.

> "Puppies are born with a functioning sense of smell (though they are born blind and deaf), and most old dogs lose their sense of hearing and eyesight but maintain their sense of smell until they die, so [in my opinion ], it's the most important sense!" — Silke Wittig, BA

Time spent forest bathing is essential for a dog's well-being.

> "When domestic dogs are permitted to go out and do what they have been bred to do, they often seem to be very satisfied, sated. When herding dogs get to herd, they can then relax. When terriers get to rat, they can then relax for a bit instead of making their owners crazy. The opportunity to get out and use that sense is something so many modern day domesticated dogs don't get enough of an opportunity to do." — Ali Brown, M.Ed., CPDT-KA, CDBC [13]

Henry David Thoreau said:

**"I think that I cannot preserve my health and spirits, unless I spend four hours a day at least—and it is commonly more than that—sauntering through the woods and over the hills and fields, absolutely free from all worldly engagements."** — Henry David Thoreau

"[Thoreau] was able to represent walking as a practice that brought mind and body into alignment: the best way to leave the distractions of everyday life behind and seek out the wild wisdom of the more-than-human world," writes Karla Armbruster in her essay *Walking with Thoreau in Mind and Dogs on Leash.* I couldn't agree more, and I have to say I experience this rebalancing of mind and body after forest bathing.

For people, spending time in nature, and particularly the forest, has many benefits. Here are a few quick highlights.

- Decreases stress, anxiety, depression, rumination.
- Increases heart rate variability, concentration, memory and creativity.
- Boosts our immune systems by increasing the NK cells (a type of white blood cell) in our blood.
- Naturally activates the nervous system's relaxation response restoring us to the parasympathetic state effortlessly.

If you want to read more about the many human-nature-health connections, I always recommend Florence Williams' book, *The Nature Fix: Why Nature Makes Us Happier, Healthier, and More Creative,* for a great summary of research. Williams begins her book discussing research done by the Japanese scientists on forest bathing or as it's called in Japan, *shinrin yoku.* She writes:

"The Japanese scientists are in the vanguard of knowing how green spaces soothe the body and brain…scientists in Japan are measuring what's actually happening to our cells and neurons... they're using field tests, hormone analysis, and new brain imaging technology to uncover how the magic works on a molecular level."

These are a few of my favorite other sources that provide a great summary of the research being done and the results. More research is needed, especially research that can link how the forest's well-being is connected with our own well-being. There is so much research available on the internet in places like PubMed and other published journal sites.

**1. A website:**
Immerse Yourself in a Forest for Better Health, New York Department of Conservation:  dec.ny.gov/lands/90720.html

**2. A book:**
The Nature Fix: Why Nature Makes Us Happier, Healthier, and More Creative, by Florence Williams (see the Resources section in the back of the book for a list of other recommended reading)

**3. Published research:**
*Shinrin-Yoku* (Forest bathing) and Nature Therapy: A State-of-the-Art Review, Margaret M. Hansen,* Reo Jones and Kirsten Tocchini. Academic Editors Yoshifumi Miyazaki, Hiromitsu Kobayashi, Sin-Ae Park, and Chorong Song: ncbi.nlm.nih.gov/pmc/articles/PMC5580555/

> "What started as an intuitive-based therapy has become an evidence-based therapy, and can now be considered to be a preventative

medicine" — Yoshifumi Miyazaki, Shinrin Yoku: The Japanese Art of Forest Bathing

"Nature as medicine. Although the simple act of walking in a forest might now seem extraordinary, the benefits that people experience during and after a session of forest therapy really are." — Yoshifumi Miyazaki, Shinrin Yoku: The Japanese Art of Forest Bathing

**Healthy Forests—Healthy Dogs—Healthy People**

> **"...our lives are increasingly informed by**
> **our growing networks of relatedness"**
>
> — M. Amos Clifford

By being in relationship with the land and with each other, not viewing each other solely as resources, our collective health and well-being increase. When we're in relationship, we care for each other. When we care for each other, we are all healthier.

> **"People protect what they love."**
>
> — Jacques-Yves Cousteau

## "Take it to the Forest"

## Forest Bathing is
## Restorative for Our Dogs

Maximizing the benefits:

- Go for walks often with your dog.

- Allow time for exercise but also time for wandering slowly where you don't need to go far.

- Take forest bathing or "smell walks," as Alexandra Horowitz calls them.

- Provide extended periods where you allow your dog to sniff and engage their other senses.

- Allow yourself to wander, slow down, sniff, look, touch, listen, and perhaps even taste.

- Notice the before and after effects for your dog and you and tell others.

- The well-being of our dogs, ourselves, and the forest are all interconnected, and the health and well-being of one benefits the health of the others.

# Section 4

## Let's Go Outside!

In this next section, Juliet and I share our Forest Bathing Field Guide followed by sharing some stories of things you can try. We also touch on forest bathing with family and friends, creativity and forest bathing, and forest bathing in a variety of environments. These activities, or invitations if you will, are meant to be playful as well as offer a doorway to exploring the forest in a new way and building a relationship with the land in your own way. Allow yourself to be invited by your dog and the forest. They are not assignments or exercises to be done a certain way. Try them and make them your own. Do them in a way that is comfortable and enjoyable for you. How ever you do them will be exactly the right way.

### Forest Bathing Field Guide

- Getting Ready: See the list of "What to Bring" at the end of this section.
- *Download a printable pocket size version of our Field Guide at nenft.com/get-field-guide.

**Where to Go:**
You can forest bathe in many places, and it is wonderful to explore new places. It is also a good idea to be attuned to what places you are drawn to the most. I personally love a combination of forest and meadow. You may remember I began Section-1 with a story of being in just such a place. You may discover over time a particular place or type of landscape that you find particularly enjoyable and restorative. Notice and pay attention to this.

**When to begin:**
When on a walk or hike, exactly when to start is entirely up to you and it may also depend on how much excess energy you and/or your dog have. There is no right or wrong here. Rather, it is about doing what feels right for you, your body, and mind. I recommend letting both your dog, and perhaps yourself, burn off some energy first. Give yourselves some time to just arrive where you are, wherever that may be. If you and your dog are arriving at the trail in the mood to begin right away, then by all means do. It may also be that you sense a starting-point for forest bathing after you've hiked or wandered for a while. There is often a natural starting point that just emerges on its own if you tune in to letting it emerge naturally.

**How to Begin:**

**"Work with the forest as a partner, rather than a setting for activity."**

— M. Amos Clifford

1. Begin by simply setting the intention to begin. Be clear with yourself that you are going to allow yourself to forest bathe for a time and that you will flow with whatever the forest or your dog offers. Let yourself use

78

your senses to follow your curiosity and enjoyment just as your dog does.

2. Notice how your dog begins.

   a. They begin noticing their surroundings, engaging each of their senses, and interacting with their surroundings through smell, hearing, sight, touch, taste, and intuition.

   b. They pause frequently.

   c. Observe your dog and how their senses bring them into contact with the land.

3. Engage each of your senses and interact with your surroundings. How does this bring you into contact with the forest? There is no right or wrong here.

> **"Let your body be your guide.**
> **Listen to where it wants to take you.**
> **Follow your nose. And take your time.**
> **It doesn't matter if you don't get anywhere."**
>
> — Dr. Quing Li author of
> *Forest bathing: How Trees Can Help You Find Health and Happiness*

## Exploring the Senses and Other Forest Bathing Activities: Some ideas

- Look around. What catches your eye? Look at things close up. Linger and look further.

- Listen to the birdsong and other sounds. What pleases you?

- Smell a handful of earth or crush some pine needles and inhale the scent.

- Taste the air with your tongue.

- Touch the bark of a tree, some moss, a rock, or water.

- Wander slowly. Pause often or just stop and stand or sit for a time.

- Explore. What can your dog show you?

- Collect some found objects and create something.

**"Not knowing the name of the tree,**
**I stood in the flood of its sweet scent"**

— Matsuo Basho

**Forest Bathing Tips: The flow of forest bathing with your dog**

- Allow your dog to set the pace and pause when they do. Take the opportunity to look around during these pauses.

- Offer pauses of your own. Slow your dog down. TIP: This is one of the places that you may have to work with your dog over time so they know what to expect when you pause. If your dog follows your lead, this is a great time to reward them. Be patient if they don't immediately follow your lead. They will learn.

- Your dog can be your guide to sensory connection. Watch them. Let them be an inspiration and explore the surroundings in your own way.

- Let yourself be playful and free from self-consciousness just as your dog is. Give yourself a "play-bow."

- Follow your enjoyment and curiosity and let it all soak in.

- When you find a place to sit, allow time for each of you to settle in. Let your dog do a bit of exploring and perhaps even watch how they arrive in this place you've chose to sit. What are they noticing that you haven't yet? If they seem antsy to move on, offer them a gentle cue to settle and relax. Share your own relaxing energy with them by authentically exuding it. Allow time.

- Leave your phone in your pocket or turn it off. Just be with what you are noticing and experiment with not photographing everything.
- Forest bathing is its own practice as is yoga or meditation. Your practice will develop over time for both you and your dog.

> **"Don't let concepts such as 'mindfulness' or 'walking meditation' trick you into making efforts to experience anything other than what the forest offers."**
>
> — M. Amos Clifford

**How Long to Forest Bathe**:

This depends on how much time you have. A minimum of 20-30 minutes and up to two or more hours is recommended, but if you only have 5-10 minutes or just the moments while you and your dog pause along your walk, then that is what you have. Take full advantage of the moments you do have. Let it be what it will be. Forest bathing is a practice that develops over time. It is different every time you are outside. As you explore with your senses, rest in just letting it take you wherever it does. This is the beauty of forest bathing.

> **"Stay for two hours if possible (though you will begin to notice the effects after twenty minutes)."**
>
> — Dr. Qing Li

**How to Finish a Forest Bathing Session:**

- Set an intention, finish, and mark it in whatever way feels right to you.

- I mostly let the land and the moment let me know how to incorporate the day's moments of forest bathing. Sometimes I make or do something and other times I just feel complete and ready to move on with Juliet. How ever you mark the end, just take a moment to acknowledge your forest bathing for that day.

**What to Bring: Consider the following:**

- Wear comfortable clothing and bring one more layer that you think you'll need because you will be moving more slowly.

- Bring something to sit on and perhaps something for your dog too, if it is cold or wet.

- Bring a sunhat, sunblock, and water if it's hot.

- Bring insect repellent or a mosquito net to cover your hat and head.

- Bring hand warmers, toe warmers, ski-pants, extra layers, and something warm to drink if it is cold.

- Bring an umbrella, poncho, or rain gear if it is raining. Forest bathing in the rain can be amazing.

## Stories of Forest Bathing

Here are some stories of forest bathing moments from Juliet, myself, and some friends while forest bathing with their dogs. As your own forest bathing explorations unfold, be careful not to create assignments for yourself that must be done in a particular way. Allow yourself to be invited by your senses. Follow your enjoyment, curiosity and playfulness. Recall Mary Oliver's words, "You only have to let the soft animal of your body love what it loves."

**Explore the forest with your sense of smell**

*Reflections from Juliet*: Stop to sniff something is my favorite thing. Have you ever dug a head-size hole, put your whole face in the hole, and breathed in deeply? I encourage you to give it a try. If dirt goes up your nose, just snort it out, and with your head still in the hole, breathe in deeply again. It's amazing! If this sounds a bit too intense try this modified version: Scoop up a small handful of earth and gently inhale. What do you notice?

*Reflections from Nadine*: I am noticing that I can smell spring-sunshine as it warms the dried leaves and that when I smell a handful of fresh dirt, it gives me a good feeling and I feel nourished in some way. Sometimes I can sense the presence of water as I approach a small stream with my sense of smell and feel the change in the air on my skin.

**Something to chew on**: I wonder what it is like for Juliet as she investigates the world through her sense of smell? I imagine it might be like being able to see individual scents, each one distinct with its own color and texture.

85

Did you know the aroma of dirt/earth is beneficial for us and contains anti-bacterial and anti-viral properties?[14]

More explorations with scent:

- If you follow your nose, where does it lead you?
- What scents do you notice when you tilt your nose up and turn in different directions?
- Pause to smell and sip the forest air.
- Explore the scents of different plants and trees and how their scents might change with the different times of day or the seasons.
- Explore the scents closer to the ground at the same level as your dog experiences them.

---------------------------------------

**Notice how your dog notices the forest**

*Reflections from Candace, Luna's mom*: "One of the best moments was when Luna was exploring an old stone wall. She spent considerable time sticking her nose into all the spaces between the rocks—and snorting and smelling in a highly attentive way. It actually made me think of the way human detectives seek clues regarding who has been in a place and what has happened there. I loved participating as a silent sharer in Luna's quest to explore the inner spaces of the stone wall. I felt very attuned to her, and I believe she felt the same toward me."

*Reflections from Sue and Ron, Brooke's mom and dad*: Brooke consistently amazed and impressed us with her complete sensory awareness of the natural environment while walking. She was the first to alert us to a hidden gift. Her sudden stop, quick head turn, laser focus, and if needed, an always impressive pointer stance to guide us to the exact location. She could hear the grouse walking in the brush, see the slightest movements happening around us, and follow scent cones, high and low, using her preferred sense of smell.

*Reflections from Leigha, Frankie's mom*: Frankie has always been rather enchanted by tall grasses - no matter where we are (whether it be a landscaped city sidewalk, a prairie, or a forest), if there is a patch of tall grasses, she will point her long, slender snout forward and push her way through them as she continues on her path. It's been an inspiration to me to always reach out and touch what calls to me on my path as I walk.

*Reflections from Pam, Cora the puppy's mom*: I watched Cora walk up to a lady slipper and just take a little sniff. It's almost as if she knew they are endangered. It is really amazing watching a puppy and just walking through the woods looking through their eyes. It's like walking through the woods with the eyes of a child.

**Something to chew on**: Often, Juliet is not only my guide in wandering off trail or investigating something, she is my guide in giving me reminders to experience and explore things with my senses.

> **"[This] is a practice in which our dogs can be our guides."**
>
> — Karla Armbruster author of *Walking with Thoreau in Mind and Dogs on Leash*

----------------------------------------

**Wander letting your senses or intuition lead the way: I wonder what you might discover?**

*Reflections from Juliet:* Hearing a sound, we broke a trail down a snowy path, then followed a scent along a stone wall through the woods, let animal tracks guide us to a stream, and wandered along its snowy banks back to the trail. Mom and I often let our sense of curiosity or intuition guide us through the forest from one thing to another.

*Reflections from Nadine:* I wandered a bit and came to a grove of young oak trees reaching towards the sky and felt a strength and open quality from them. I sat on a log and felt the warmth of the sun. The birdsong was pleasant here and made me smile as I closed my eyes and listened. I noticed some pine sap on a fallen pine cone and enjoyed its sticky fresh scent, inhaling it deeply. I notice that when I allow my whole body to lead me, my mind quiets and there is a sense of knowing and being a part of the forest. If I feel a pull to go in a direction, I allow myself to follow that pull and be led to an awaiting discovery.

**Something to chew on**: Have you ever just felt a pull to go in a certain direction? Allow yourself to follow that pull or just flow from one sense to the next as your curiosity invites you.

> **"Intuition is a sense, just like sight or smell, a perception that brings you information. It comes to you as a still small voice, an instinctive action, a flash of creativity, or a moment when you are one with the world. You suddenly know something without the use of analytical processes; the knowledge is just there."**
>
> — Sharon Franquemont author of
> *Intuition: Your Electric Self: Creating a Life Path of Illumination*

**Pause with your dog and use your senses to notice**

*Reflections from Pam, Cora the puppy's mom*: Cora brought me back to the basics of forest therapy. As we've been traveling the trails it is so cool to watch her discover, notice and take little pauses. I've learned to stop again, to listen, to notice. Just to watch her discover ferns and roots is a pleasure and invites me to make my own discoveries along the trail.

*Reflections from Nadine*: Juliet was rooting around on an old log and as I waited for her, I spied a young pine tree backlit by the sun with many little glistening spider webs in it. Some of the spider webs were these perfect round discs about six inches across in diameter shimmering beautifully in the morning sun. Juliet finished investigating, and we meandered on our way down the trail to find something else.

*Reflections from Linda, Leela's mom*: Whenever I walk with Leela, I'm aware of how differently we use our senses compared to our animal companions. When her ears perk up or she suddenly lifts her nose to sky, I wonder what she is hearing or smelling that I cannot hear or smell; I give it a try, anyway. She reminds me how pleasure, excitement or curiosity is shaped by our perspectives as humans in a more-than-human world, and yet, we may still stop and sniff the lilacs together in a moment that connects us through our senses.

*Reflections from Nadine*: As I paused with Juliet while she investigated a new scent, I looked around and through a window of Joe Pye weed and fall asters where there was a big stone with a natural hollow that held water with a piece of moss.

**Something to chew on**: When Juliet selects a spot to pause, I pause, too. When your dog is ready to move on, follow. You may also find that when you get interested in something along the trail, your dog will stop and wait for you until you are ready to move on. If they do, this is a great time to give your dog a reinforcer-treat of some kind if they wait without being told. "Catch your dog being the great dog they can be," says Sue Schiemer. As I pause along the trail following Juliet's lead or my own, I experience many things I would have walked right by had I not paused. I notice it feels hard at first to slow down, but then it becomes a wonderful practice and I relish each pause as a delicious moment of enjoyment and self-care.

-----------------------------------------

## Sitting: Find a spot to sit and be

*Reflections from Sue and Ron, Brooke mom and dad*: Shallow, slow moving water was a delightful sitting spot for Brooke. Whenever possible, Brooke would locate a body of water, her favorite classical element, for some tasting, touching and sitting. We are sure that Brooke possessed a "heart sense" that she used to help us connect with the world she loved. Our time in the natural world was enhanced by noticing how Brooke noticed.

*Reflections from Leigha, Frankie's mom*: I keep a sit-spot practice in my back yard, and Frankie often joins me in the practice. Once I settle in to my spot, she will leave my side and find a place of her own where she sits, contentedly, and just IS. She doesn't sleep, and she isn't overly concerned with what I'm doing. She just quietly observes all that

surrounds her - alternating between soft and focused gazing, sometimes with perked ears, sometimes with the slightest twitch of her nose catching a scent on the breeze.

*Reflections from Nadine*: Juliet and I love this spot by the stream. She is always bringing me here. We have another place that feels like it is deep in the woods and only we know about it. It's quiet, with tall trees and a flat moss-covered rock to sit on. Another spot is a crevice in a big boulder where I built a fairy house along the side of the trail. When it starts to look a little ragged I do some tending and spruce it up a bit. There are some places that just make me feel happy or uplifted and others that bring a soothing quality. Sometimes I sense a mystery. Sometimes I feel a strong sense of the people and times past when standing somewhere. Some spaces make me feel very playful and I want to build a fort or a fairy house.

**Something to chew on:** Juliet and I have found many delightful sitting spots—or rather, these spots have found us. Some we return to again and again feel like forest rooms, each with their own sense of place.

How lucky to have a companion
who so naturally and effortlessly inhabits the magic of forest bathing.
Watch. Partake. Enjoy!

**Lie in the grass with your dog**

*Reflections from Nadine:* I am noticing on this August evening that the grass has a subtle warm scent in the evening sun. I can feel both the warm sun and the cool evening shadows as I move my hands and bare feet through the grass. The birds are settling down for the evening and a sense of calm is drifting in and holding everything gently. I love coming home from work and simply joining Juliet in the backyard, plopping down beside her in the grass.

*Reflections from Juliet:* I remember an evening last summer. Mom arrived home and after greeting dad, she came out to see me. Without getting up, I greeted her with a stretch and squinted my eyes together. This was my way of inviting her to come enjoy the cool grass with me. She peeled off her shoes and socks and sat down in the grass next to me. I plopped my head back down into the grass and let out a big sigh. Cool grass is perhaps the most perfect pillow there is. I heard mom let out a sigh as she started to relax and watched her enjoy the feel of the cool grass on her bare feet. It doesn't take long and she's stretched out beside me. We just lay there for a while, feeling the coolness of the grass, smelling the mix of earthy, green scents of the grass, enjoying the fading sun, and listening to the birds. After a while, we seemed to melt into the rhythm of the yard. A rabbit came out and was having a snack of the lawn, too. Lying in the grass is a personal favorite of mine. It is right up there with digging a hole on my list of favorite things to do.

**Something to chew on**: The best forest bathing activities are often the simplest!

Forest Bathing in the Park, Garden or Anywhere!

**"You can forest bathe anywhere in the world --
wherever there are trees [or plants]."**

—Dr. Quing Li

Sit outside your front door, lie in the grass or visit a corner of your yard and do some forest bathing. No matter where you are or the season, slow down and begin to notice. There are things to discover. The park or your garden are places for forest bathing as well. I love to sit just outside my front door and watch the birds in the forsythia bush across my driveway. I wonder what would it be like to be a plant or animal that lives in this garden? I am tended in many ways by my garden in response for the tending I give.

**"Spending time with plants really can improve
your health and well-being."**

— Yoshifumi Miyazaki author of
*Shinrin Yoku: The Japanese Art of Forest Bathing*

*Reflections on Forest Bathing in Different Landscapes*
**The Ocean - Vicky Kyan, Certified Forest Therapy Guide, Great Barrier Island, New Zealand**: "The overriding essence I notice when Nature Bathing/ Forest Bathing by the ocean is the presence of the elements—ocean/estuary, wind/breeze, sand/rocks, and sun/skies. This is raw power and beauty that shifts and changes constantly - Nature's Art Gallery - the creation of all life... and the ever-present song of the sea..."

**The Desert - Ben Page, Certified Forest Therapy Guide, Los Angeles, CA**: "The high desert is home to an incredible diversity of life cast against a resounding silence, the dramatic blue sky, and the stoic rock formations. When we slow down and awaken our senses in this environment, it connects us to an ancient wisdom that we may then see within ourselves as well, a teaching of how beauty and life interpenetrate even the most harsh environments."

**Winter Forest Bathing - Brenda Spitzer, Certified Forest Therapy Guide, Chicago, IL**: "The winter months are a special time to walk in the forest. These colder months provide the space and time to notice the quiet details of nature.  Some details are only possible to notice when temperatures drop below freezing.  Other details are made more visible by the absence of the lush green growth of the warmer months and by the special quality of winter light."

**Urban Parks - Tamrin Willey, Certified Forest Therapy Guide, Boston, MA**: "City trees have witnessed the comings and goings of many, offering homes for migrating birds and purifying the smoggy air.  These trees have ancient stories to tell, and when I slow down long enough to witness these trees as they are witnessing me, I sometimes forget I am in a city altogether.  When I slow down and let in all the sounds, I find the bird song can even drown out the sirens.  Urban parks offer refuge from fast-paced city life, and they are places where all kinds of beings come together to soak up the natural atmosphere.  Even the smallest of trees and green spaces surrounded by pavement is a world unto itself with endless possibility for connection."

## Creating Forest Art and Play

I love to collect things as I wander and create things. It's the little kid and the artist in me coming out. What supplies does the forest offer to inspire you? Following are some ideas but you can make anything, big or small: fairy forts, mandalas, abstract designs, something to honor something or someone.

I came across these bits of pine cone on top of this rock that a squirrel had left after removing the seeds. They were the perfect art materials and pallet. Note: Be respectful, create using found objects and ask before picking leaves or flowers.

**"It is a happy talent to know how to play."**

— Ralph Waldo Emerson

## Forest Bathing with Family and Friends

As my mom and I would stroll in the woods, she would point out things she was drawn to. I remember her delighting in the many shades of green and particularly the vivid green of moss and early spring. After a rain, she would take great pleasure in the color of the dark wet tree bark and how it stood out against the green backdrop of the forest. We would look, touch, be curious, and enjoy the pleasure that we found.

**"It only takes a moment to make a moment."**

— Unknown

My personal experience has been very, very powerful and these are some of my most cherished memories of my family. I may not have acknowledged them when I was young, but as an adult now, I remember them clearly and carry them with me close to my heart. There is something very profound about sharing what we notice  with others and being heard.

- Sharing with each other incorporates our experiences.
- Sharing our own connections and relationship with nature and each other makes the bonds stronger in a wonderful way than when we just keep our thoughts to ourselves.
- Our connections with each other and the forest are strengthened through the simple act of sharing and realizing that we are noticing both similar and different things.

It's tempting to talk the whole time when walking with friends and family. Try something new. After catching up for a bit, suggest walking in silence for 5-10 minutes (or longer if you wish). You may be met with an odd look so this is where you have to channel your inner dog and not be shy. Take this opportunity to build lifelong memories.

**Feeling shy about forest bathing with others?**
**Dogs rarely worry about shyness.**

— Juliet

## Tips for Forest bathing with Friends and Family

- Walk or find a spot to sit and simply notice what's going on in the forest around you.

- Keep the silence for a time.

- Sitting apart is fine, but it can also be fun to sit side-by-side or back-to-back.

- Two people looking at the same view can notice very different things.

- Sometimes it can help to just focus on one of the senses like listening, smelling or touch.

- After the 10 (or 20) minutes is up, share what you've each noticed with each other. There is no right or wrong here. Just allow each person to have their turn to share while the other is silently listening. Resist the urge to jump in or respond while the other person is talking. If you have more than two people, you can try using a sharing piece that you pass around. The person with the sharing piece is the only one talking and the other person listens until it's their turn.

**Create with Family or Friends**

Collect found objects individually and build something together. It doesn't need to be anything in particular. Just take turns placing the found objects next to each other and see what emerges. As a certified forest therapy guide, I've guided many families on forest bathing outings, and the highlight of the walk is almost always creating something together. The creation can take any form and have a different meaning or purpose for each person. The main thing is that it's fun to do and each contributor adds what they want, in their own way. Parents, let go of outcomes here, and just play. As adults, we've forgotten how much fun it can be to play in the forest with family or friends and to let ourselves be free.

> **"Only a few, who remain children at heart, can ever find that fair, lost path again to fairyland."**
>
> — L.M. Montgomery, The Story Girl

## "Take it to the Forest"

### Let's Go Outside!

- Create memories with family and friends.
- Let your creativity flow forth in the forest.
- Try forest bathing in different places.
- Share your stories of forest bathing moments with others.
- Take advantage of our field guide. Download it at nenft.com/get-field-guide

**Share your stories of forest bathing.**
**What you are noticing?**

Use the journal pages at the end of this book or share online at nenft.com/dogstories

## Bonus Section

## Forest Bathing with Cats

**"Time spent with cats is never wasted" — Sigmund Freud**

*In Juliet's Words*
Forest bathing with your cat can present a unique set of challenges. Chief among them, is you are dealing with cats. Personally, I have found it's very hard to do much of anything with cats, especially when we're outside. All I want to do is chase them. I wonder if you'll experience this same urge? Perhaps it's different for humans and you don't have the same urge to chase cats. It can be dangerous to chase cats.

That said, I know there are a lot of cat lovers out there, and if you are one of them, I don't want to leave you out. Forest bathing is for everyone. And with cats, it can be a wonderful practice. Although, I do have to be clear that nothing done with a cat can ever be as good as doing it with a dog. I just want to bark loud and clear on this point.

My housemate, Cleopatra the Cat, and mom do forest bathing together in the garden. Cleopatra is a white and black cat in her elder years and likes to wander about the garden watching birds and following butterflies and the like. Cleopatra feels because she is older than me, I should give her seniority in the house, but I'm not buying it. She's got a bit of a princess mentality, if you ask me. The forest bathing usually begins with mom watching and then wandering with Cleopatra. Cleopatra saunters by mom swishing her tail hypnotically in that way that cats do. As they wander along, Mom starts by just watching Cleopatra, the way she moves and seeing what interests her. Then the adventure begins.

Mom, Cleopatra, and I were in the garden. The morning was cool and the dew was still on the grass. There was an earthy scent in the air and a more distant scent of honeysuckle from the front of the house. Mom was doing some weeding and I was helping out, digging a hole nearby. I love weeding! As I plopped down into the hole I'd just finished digging and was enjoying the pleasure of the cool earth on my belly, Cleopatra scampered by following a cricket she had disturbed from its roost—hop—stalk—stop—hop—stalk—stop—hop—stalk—stop—pounce—miss. Start over again. Mom paused her weeding and watched Cleopatra as she followed the cricket. The sound of a hummingbird buzzed by like a mini-plane as it zoomed in to drink nectar from the garden flowers. Other birds were in the midst of their morning chorus. It was good to be in the company of all the plant and animal beings as we all did our morning chores. I stood up, moved some dirt around in my hole and plopped back down. Ah, weeding. The smell of the dirt was lovely and the cool feel of it on my belly was welcome. Mom was watching a butterfly now. She and Cleopatra were just watching, noticing, taking it all in.

**Indoors** is another situation altogether however. Somehow, Cleopatra and I are able to sit peacefully, side-by-side in front of the window. Side-by-side, we sit or lay watching the happenings on the other side of the glass. I remember a sunny fall day when Cleopatra and I we're lying in the sun next to the sliding glass door in our living room. We were both relaxed and drowsy, alternating napping and gazing out the window at the goings-on.

There were leaves rustling and blowing around that kept catching Cleopatra's attention. Have you noticed cats tend to get distracted by just about anything? I was watching her ears perk up and then relax over and over again. It was quite amusing. Then we both noticed two robins splashing in the bird bath. They were having a grand time.  The sound of the water splashing was refreshing somehow and reminded me of wading in the pond and the feel of the cool water covering my belly. This reminded me of when Mom and I go to the stream. The mud squishing between my toes or just sitting. Relaxing. Noticing. Letting our attention follow the goings-on outdoors as we listen to the sounds and feel the warmth of the sun. Cleopatra was still watching the robins, so I took the opportunity to chew on her catnip mouse for a while. MMM, it was tasty!

One of the best ways of forest bathing with your cat or dog is simply to take cues from them. What are they inviting you to notice? Follow your cat through the garden or just hang out and do what they do. What are you noticing? Follow your own attention noticing through the lens of your senses. Use all your senses and be fully in your human or canine body, whichever you have.

# "Take it to the Forest"

## Forest Bathing with Cats

Some fun things to try for forest bathing with a cat:

**Indoors:**

- Enjoy the sun coming in through a window.
- Watch the birds outside.
- Watch the leaves or snowflakes falling.
- Notice movement with all of your senses.

**Outdoors**: If you have an outdoor cat, go for a walk together. Follow your cat. What are they drawn to? Also do some investigating or playing of your own.

- Lie in the grass and soak up the sun.
- Let movement, sound and smells capture your attention.
- Play with a bug.
- Watch an ant crawling in the grass.

# About Guided Group Forest Bathing Walks

*Reflections from group forest bathing participants*

> **"I will forever walk through the fields and forests with heightened sensations and appreciations. Thank you!" -- DL and Lucy**

> **"This is a wonderful way to become more present in your life, in nature. What a gift! Reminded me of being a child and looking through her eyes." — Kathy L.**

The practice of forest bathing develops and deepens over time and just like other well-being practices such as yoga and meditation, having an instructor and guide is helpful and supportive. A guide frees you to let go of time, fully immerse yourself in the experience and to slow down. When I attend a series of classes, it gives me permission to take this time for myself in a way that I don't always feel when forest bathing on my own.

> **"A guide can help you to slow down, to connect you with nature and let the forest do its therapeutic work. Walking with a guide who is a trained forest therapist can help you feel more comfortable and find the right environment to fit your needs." — Dr. Quing Li**

## "Take it to the Forest"

## Attending Guided Group Forest Bathing Programs

- Register for a local forest bathing class or workshop led by a Certified Forest Therapy Guide

- **Nadine's Workshops**: Visit my website, nenft.com , to see what trainings Juliet and I are running. We regularly hold "Forest bathing With Your Dog" workshops as well as many other forest bathing programs just for people. We hope you'll join us!

- **Find a certified guide or instructor near you**: Use this worldwide guide locator map to find a Certified Forest Therapy Guide or forest bathing program near you. forestbathing.info/find-a-guide.html.

- **Become A Certified Forest Therapy Guide**: If you are interested in training to become a Certified Forest Therapy Guide, visit natureandforesttherapy.org. The Association of Nature and Forest Therapy Guides and Programs conducts training all over the world and has the most in depth and tested curriculum. The certification program is recognized and respected worldwide and includes the seven-day training and a six-month practicum. Granted, I'm a bit biased, but truly, it's a fantastic training!

# A Very Brief History of Forest Bathing

### *Shinrin Yoku* and Forest Therapy

The Japanese were experiencing a tech-boom in the 1980s and an equally large spike in stress-related illnesses occurred. One of the ways the Japanese Ministry of Health responded was by researching how spending time under the forest canopy affected health and well-being. They took portable laboratories out to the forest and tested the effects of spending time under the forest canopy in specific forests. The results were impressive and more research continues. The Japanese Ministry of Health responded to the research by creating Forest Medicine Centers in the forests where research had shown a positive impact on visitors' health and well-being. There are now more than sixty forest medicine centers in Japan and even more in South Korea.

In the United States, inspired by the Japanese practice of *shinrin yoku* and his other life experience, M. Amos Clifford founded the Association of Nature and Forest Therapy Guides and Programs (ANFT) in 2011. His aim was to share this practice and establish it around the globe for the benefit of **both** forests and humans. At the time this book was published, the ANFT has trained over 700 forest therapy guides worldwide and is adding hundreds more each year.

### An Ancient Practice of Being and Healing in Nature

The practice of forest bathing or humans working with nature, being in relationship with nature seeking restoration and healing is really an ancient

practice that we all seek intuitively and is part of our DNA. Humans evolved in nature as sensory beings. All our ancestors were in relationship with the land as they evolved for millennia. So, in this way forest bathing is really a very old practice. Our modern version of forest bathing is really a return to or remembering of what our bodies, minds and hearts need to help them be healthy, to recover from stress or to feel ourselves.

> **"Throughout our evolution, we've spent 99.9 percent of our time in natural environments. Our physiological functions are still adapted to it. During everyday life, a feeling of comfort can be achieved if our rhythms are synchronized with those of the environment."**
>
> — Yoshifumi Miyazaki

Juliet reminds me that I am still a sensory being every time we go out. All I need to do is allow myself the pleasure of returning to this way of being. This re-connection to using our senses may seem new to some of us modern-humans, but dogs are doing this all the time.

> **"Humans are not separate from nature... Healing of people and forests happens together... The medicine that brings healing is in the relationship."**
>
> — M. Amos Clifford

# Resources, Research and Recommended Reading

**Cancer Support Related Resources**

- Virginia Thurston Healing Garden: The Healing Garden Cancer Support Center is a beautiful facility located on 8 acres of woodlands and gardens that help promote resiliency and recovery. (healinggardensupport.org)

**Dog Related Resources**

- Calming Signals - The Art of Survival: en.turid-rugaas.no/calming-signals—the-art-of-survival.html

- *On Talking Terms With Dogs: Calming Signals* by Turid Rugaas (en.turid-rugaas.no)

- The "settle" cue
  - Video: smartdoguniversity.com/teach-dog-settle
  - More: smartdoguniversity.com/?s=settle
  - Article: whole-dog-journal.com/behavior/teach-your-dog-to-settle-down

- Whole Dog Journal: whole-dog-journal.com

- Find a certified dog trainer:
  - Karen Pryor Academy, find-a-trainer: karenpryoracademy.com/find-a-trainer/#!directory/map
  - The Association of Professional Dog Trainers: apdt.com
  - Certification Council for Professional Dog Trainers: ccpdt.org/dog-owners/certified-dog-trainer-directory

- Tellington Touch for dogs: ttouch.com

- Silke Wittig, BA, CPDT-KSA, CBCC-KA, CNWI

HeRo Canine Consulting LLC: herocanineconsulting.com

- Ali Brown, M.Ed., CPDT-KA, CDBC and author of *Scaredy Dog!* Great Companions, LLC: greatcompanions.info

**Forest Therapy Related Resources**

- New England Nature and Forest Therapy Consulting: Provides a variety of Forest Therapy programs. nenft.com (Nadine's website)

- Association of Nature and Forest Therapy Guides and Programs (ANFT) The world's leading provider of forest therapy guide training. natureandforesttherapy.org

- Shinrin-yoku.org: shinrin-yoku.org

**Safety Related Resources**

- Poison ivy/ poison oak resources: youtu.be/4oyoDRHpQK0

- Preventing tick bites and tick information: tickencounter.org

- Pet First Aid: If you want to learn more about pet first aid, the Red Cross has an online course and a free app. Download the app. The free Pet First Aid app provides instant access to expert guidance on how to maintain your pet's health, what to do in emergencies, and how to include pets in your emergency preparedness plans.

**Reading**

- *Your Guide to Forest Bathing: Experience the Healing Power of Nature,* by M. Amos Clifford

- *Braiding Sweetgrass: Indigenous Wisdom, Scientific Knowledge and the Teachings of Plants,* by Robin Wall Kimmerer

- *The Hidden Life of Trees: What They Feel, How They Communicate — Discoveries from A Secret World,* by Peter Wohlleben

- *What a Plant Knows: A Field Guide to the Senses*, by Daniel Chamovitz

- *Forest Bathing: How Trees Can Help You Find Health and Happiness*, by Qing Li

- *Shinrin Yoku: The Japanese Art of Forest Bathing*, by Yoshifumi Miyazaki

- *The Joy of Forest Bathing:Reconnect With Wild Places & Rejuvenate Your Life*, by Melanie Choukas-Bradley

- *The Nature Fix: Why Nature Makes Us Happier, Healthier, and More Creative*, by Florence Williams

- *Intelligence in Nature: An Inquiry into Knowledge*, by Jeremy Narby

- *Wild Geese*, by Mary Oliver

- *Scaredy Dog! Understanding & Rehabilitating Your Reactive Dog*, by Ali Brown

- *On Talking Terms With Dogs: Calming Signals* by Turid Rugaas (en.turid-rugaas.no) This book is listed twice because it's that good and important.

## Research Dogs

- Sensory stimulation as environmental enrichment for captive animals: A review, Deborah L.Wells: https://www.sciencedirect.com/science/article/abs/pii/S0168159109000057

- Long-term stress levels are synchronized in dogs and their owners, Ann-Sofie Sundman, Enya Van Poucke, Ann-Charlotte Svensson Holm, Åshild Faresjö, Elvar Theodorsson, Per Jensen & Lina S. V. Roth https://www.nature.com/articles/s41598-019-43851-x

## Research Humans

- The ANFT website has a great selection of research articles. (natureandforesttherapy.org/about/science)

- *Shinrin-Yoku* (Forest bathing) and Nature Therapy: A State-of-the-Art Review, Margaret M. Hansen,* Reo Jones and Kirsten Tocchini. Academic Editors Yoshifumi Miyazaki, Hiromitsu Kobayashi, Sin-Ae Park, and Chorong Song: ncbi.nlm.nih.gov/pmc/articles/PMC5580555/

- Forest adjuvant anti-cancer therapy to enhance natural cytotoxicity in urban women with breast cancer: A preliminary prospective interventional study, Byungho J.KimaHyewonJeongaSujinParkbSungjae Lee : sciencedirect.com/science/article/abs/pii/S1876382015300111

- Characteristics and distribution of terpenes in South Korean forests, Jaeseok Lee, Kyoung Sang Cho, Youngjae Jeon, Ji Beom Kim, Young-ran Lim, Kyungho Lee and Im-Soon Lee: https://jecoenv.biomedcentral.com/articles/10.1186/s41610-017-0038-z

Much more research is available online. Try these websites to start, and search for terms such as *"shinrin-yoku,"* "forest bathing," "forest medicine" and "forest therapy."

- US National Library of Medicine National Institutes of Health : https://www.ncbi.nlm.nih.gov/pubmed/

- ScienceDirect: https://www.sciencedirect.com/

# Endnotes

1. M. Amos Clifford, author of *Your Guide to Forest Bathing: Experience the Healing Power of Nature* and Founder of The Association of Nature and Forest Therapy Guides and Programs

2. *Forest Bathing 101: An Interview with Melanie Choukas-Bradley*, by Leigh Stringer.

3. *Intelligence in Nature: An Inquiry into Knowledge,* by Jeremy Narby according to Dr. Toshiyuki Nakagaki

4. Line from the Mary Oliver poem *Wild Geese*

5. Stanley Core, PhD, DSc, FRSC, *How Dogs Read Human Body Language: Is your dog reading you like a book?* Summarization, Nadine Mazzola, 2019

6. Rebecca A. Johnson, PhD, director of the Research Center for Human Animal Interaction at University of Missouri, nbcnews.com/better/health/why-dogs-help-us-feel-good-help-us-cope-life-ncna799656

7. Bachelor of Veterinary Medicine & Surgery (University of Edinburgh, Scotland), Certificate in Veterinary Radiology, Member of Royal College of Veterinary Surgeons

8. Pete Wedderburn, BVM&S CertVR MRCVS , Bachelor of Veterinary Medicine & Surgery (University of Edinburgh, Scotland), Certificate in Veterinary Radiology, Member of Royal College of Veterinary Surgeons

9. M. Amos Clifford author of *Your Guide to Forest Bathing: Experience the Healing Power of Nature*

10.  Oxford American Writer's Thesaurus

11.  Line from the Mary Oliver poem *Wild Geese*

12.  Applied Animal Behaviour Science Journal, *Sensory stimulation as environmental enrichment for [dogs]*: 12 A review by Deborah L. Wells. School of Psychology, Queen's University Belfast, Ireland, UK

13.  Certified Professional Dog Trainer-Knowledge Assessed (CPDT-KA) , Certified Dog Behavior Consultant (CDBC)

14.  *The healing powers of the earth*, Barbara Damrosch, April 23, 2015, washingtonpost.com/lifestyle/home/savoring-that-earthy-smell/2015/04/22/b42c096e-e1f3-11e4-81ea-0649268f729e_story. *The Smell of Living Soil*, Sheila Keeling, NRCS Natural Resource Planner in the Hopkinsville, KY Work Unit, nrcs.usda.gov/wps/portal/nrcs/detail/ky/soils/health/?cid=nrcseprd376407

# Acknowledgements

Thank you to everyone who helped me write this book, whether you knew it or not. It has been an amazing journey. As I'm writing these acknowledgements I'm smiling and thinking how cool it is that I have gotten to this point in the writing of this book.

I have to start by thanking my husband Jerry who has been encouraging me from the first moment I shared the idea for this book with him. His instinct as well as his gentle reminders to stop tweaking things have been my north star.

Thank you to my family who each in their own way offered love, encouragement and support by both reading and not reading early versions of the manuscript and especially to my dad, a writer himself, who helped me maintain the perseverance that it takes to actually keep writing something.

M. Amos Clifford, author of *Your Guide to Forest Bathing: Experience the Healing Power of Nature*, for founding the Association of Nature and Forest Therapy Guides and Programs and creating the framework for the ANFT model of Forest Therapy. For taking all my calls as I was contemplating this training, even when I asked "is this a bunch of people in the woods hugging trees?"

To my fellow Forest Therapy Guides, I am so honored to be on this path with you all and a part of this global forest family. And a special thanks to those of you who directly contributed to this book.

Melanie Choukas-Bradley: You are such a dear friend to write such a thoughtful and lovely foreword for this book as you were finishing your latest book, *The Joy of Forest Bathing*. I am so grateful. It was my great pleasure to be your mentor. Lovely lilac lady indeed!

Susan Baracco of Story Architect for Women (storyarchitectforwomen.com), my editor and coach in writing this book: I am so glad to have found you. Because of your help I have a pride and belief in this book that I can feel throughout my whole body, heart and soul.

Sue Schiemer, friend and fellow forest therapy guide: You have been such a contributor to this book in connecting the dots between forest bathing and our dog's well-being. Thank you for your spirit, your generosity with your time and wise thoughtfulness. You're calm presence and encouragement as one author to another emerging author in myself has been of great benefit to me.

Phyllis Abramson: You are an inspiration. It has been my great pleasure to mentor you in forest therapy guiding and to equally learn from you. Thank you for your encouragement and wise input in writing this book and your continued support.

Carol Swerzenski: Your encouragement and willingness to read early manuscripts was such an important part of getting to this point. I so enjoyed our conversations and all those delicious Thai lunches. Thank you!

The Virginia Thurston Healing Garden: To everyone there now and everyone who has played a part in creating and growing this amazing place over the years, thank you for this place of healing and love. It has been such an important part of finding healing from my cancer journey.

My dear Sunflower Tribe: I love you all and relish the creative time we spend together and the tending we cultivate. Special thanks to Jennifer Elliott for her suggestions and reminding both Juliet and I to keep our four paws on the ground while writing this book and to Candace for your generosity and mentoring.

Robin Wall Kimmerer it has been my privilege and pleasure to encounter you both through your writing and in person. Your writing and in particular, *Witness to the Rain from Braiding Sweetgrass*, has been a inspiration in finding my own authentic writing voice.

Thank you to the many other authors who have inspired me and provided facts along the journey of writing this book and in particular: Mary Oliver (the unofficial poet laureate of forest therapy), Pat Ahern and Lisa Zschuschen authors of Forest Bathing: Living and Healing, Peter Wohlleben author of *The Hidden Life of Trees: What*

*They Feel, How They Communicate—Discoveries from A Secret World*, Daniel Chamovitz author of *What a Plant Knows: A Field Guide to the Senses*, Karla Armbruster author of *Walking with Thoreau in Mind and Dogs on Leash*, Alexandra Horowitz, author of *Inside of a Dog: What Dogs See, Smell, and Know; Sharon Franquemont author of Intuition: Your Electric Self.*.

*In Juliet's words*
My neighbor and friend, Judith, of the Yankee Golden Retriever Club and mom of Sparky and Ellie: If you ever meet Judith out on the trail, she has the best dog biscuits and is willing to share if you sit nicely for her.

My town of Acton, MA, the Acton Conservation Commission, and all of the conservation organizations that tend the land we walk on, as well as the many people who have been both nurtured by and tended this land for thousands of years. Thank you. Thanks also to Tower Hill Botanic Garden, Acton Recreation Department, the Trustees of Reservations, Fruitlands Museum, Essex County Greenbelt, Essex County Trail Association. And a special thanks to North East Animal Shelter for all the tending they do of animals in need!

*In Juliet's words*
Zephyr (and JP Sears): We don't know each other, but reading your essay in the *Dharma of Dogs*, inspired me to find my writing voice and partner with mom in writing this book. Thank you Zephyr for your whit and great wisdom.

Karen Marsh (bcdh.org.uk), Silke Wittig (herocanineconsulting.com) and Ali Brown (greatcompanions.info): Thank you for your time, wisdom and enthusiasm.

Diane Faulkner (dianefaulkner.com): Thank you for your editing prowess and helping me put the final editing touches on this book to make it shine—and for your enthusiasm.

Annabel O'Neill (annabeloneill.com): Thank you for your kick-ass videography, shooting and editing the book trailers for this project. Also for your wonderful spirit and friendship. Always a pleasure!

# About the Author

Nadine Mazzola is founder and director of New England Nature and Forest Therapy Consulting through which she does work as a Certified Forest Therapy Guide, public speaking engagements and consulting with organizations interested in forest therapy. She has been guiding forest therapy walks since 2015. She is also Co-Executive Director for the Association of Nature and Forest Therapy Guides and Programs. Nadine has been featured on PBS, ABC's Chronicle and in the Boston Globe and Boston Magazine, among others. As a cancer survivor, practicing good self-care is Nadine's most important guiding principle for herself. She has come to know the healing and support that nature can offer us through her own personal wellness journey. Nadine has a business and marketing background and was formerly a world professional pocket billiards player competing on the Women's Professional Billiard Tour. Also, an artist, she facilitates expressive arts classes often incorporating elements of forest therapy throughout. A Massachusetts native who loves spending time wandering and exploring in nature, she is joyous to be sharing forest bathing and creating environments for forest therapy. You can contact Nadine through her website: nenft.com.

## About
## New England
## Nature and Forest Therapy
## Consulting

New England Nature & Forest Therapy Consulting (NENFT) provides a variety forest therapy programs. Our passion is working with organizations introducing the wellness practice of forest bathing/forest therapy to staff or as a special event for annual staff meetings and retreats. NENFT provides consulting and presentations for organizations to incorporate forest therapy as a health and wellness modality to reduce stress and improve well-being of staff and for the creation of Certified Forest Therapy Trails. Trails are certified through the Association of Nature & Forest Therapy Guides & Programs. Contact NENFT via: nenft.com/speaking-and-presentations.

# About Blue Cloud Books
## Publisher

Blue Cloud Books is the publisher of *Forest Bathing with your Dog* and was founded by Nadine Mazzola. The name for Blue Cloud Books has a bit of a story behind it.

At one point in my life, I attend a workshop, and we were asked to draw our life map. Colorful markers of all sizes and shades were spread across a big round table like a kaleidoscope. I took a big sheet of paper and set to work or perhaps it was play. My map took on the theme of a garden, my garden. There were flowers and sweet, green grass. A watering can was added bringing the nurturing of water to help things in my garden grow. The flowers in their various phases represented the present, past and future parts of my life, my passions, my gifts to give and receive and my connections. The water represented the people and things that nurtured me along on these various journeys. Above it all I drew a sunny, blue cloud.

When I showed the map to my husband, Jerry, and had pointed out all the different parts of my garden-life-map, I hadn't mentioned the cloud and he asked me about it. I replied that I didn't know but I had a strong feeling it needed to be there. Without batting an eye, Jerry stated he knew what the cloud stood for. What?, I asked. The cloud is you when you are happy with yourself he said. That's you when you are in your element and being "you" he stated. And so the name Blue Cloud Books and this book itself represents that journey of becoming and being my authentic self. Of doing what I love and being *me*.

# Forest Bathing Journal

Use these pages for your own reflections and
stories of forest bathing.

**What you are noticing about
forest bathing with your dog?**

Share your stories online at
nenft.com/dogstories/

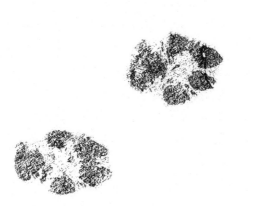

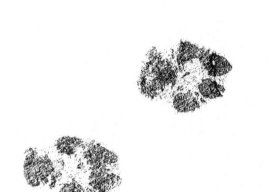

## "Take it to the Forest"

### The Author's Top Four Keys to Success

In my experience, the four biggest things to make forest bathing with your dog an enjoyable, successful, and lifelong practice are:

1. Use a 20-foot training lead for a leash so you have space to pause or wander ahead.

2. Bring your patience and playfulness to this practice. Forest bathing is a way of being.

3. Be patient while your practice develops organically with your dog over time.

4. Pay attention. Your dog is inviting you to slow down and engage all of your senses. Listen.

*Thank you little one*

Made in the USA
Las Vegas, NV
22 April 2021